CLASSIC WARPLANES

McDONNELL DOUGLAS

F-15 EAGLE

Paul Crickmore

SMITHMARK

A SALAMANDER BOOK

©Salamander Books Ltd. 1992
129-137 York Way,
London N7 9LG,
United Kingdom.
ISBN 0-8317-1408-5
This edition published in 1992 by
SMITHMARK Publishers, Inc., 112
Madison Avenue, New York, NY 10016.
SMITHMARK Books are available for
bulk purchase for sales promotion and
premium use. For details write or
telephone the Manager of Special Sales,
SMITHMARK Publishers, Inc., 112
Madison Avenue, New York, NY 10016.
(212) 532-6660.

CREDITS

Editor: Chris Westhorp
Designer: Studio Gossett
Color Artwork: ©Pilot Press Ltd.
Three-view and cutaway drawings:
©Pilot Press Ltd.
Filmset by: The Old Mill, London
Color reproduction by Graham Curtis
Repro
Printed in Belgium by Proost International
Book Production, Turnhout.

ACKNOWLEDGEMENTS

Dedicated to Mother and Father
The author offers thanks to the following:
Lee Whitney of MCAIR; Dave Peterson;
Kearney Bothwell of Hughes Radar
Systems; Irv Burrows; Mike Hurst; Bob
Munro; David Oliver; S/Sgt. Steve
Smith; Chuck Suits of Pratt & Whitney;
Gill Vale; and Dave Wilton.

AUTHOR

PAUL CRICKMORE is a National Account Development Manager with HP Bulmer Drinks Ltd. Prior to commencing a career in sales four years ago, however, he spent 13 years with the Civil Aviation Authority at the London Air Traffic Control Centre. He obtained his Private Pilots Licence 12 years ago and has maintained an avid interest in military aviation matters for as long as he can remember, having flown in eight different types of fast jet and numerous tankers and helicopters. His other books are "Lockheed SR-71 Blackbird", "SR-71 Blackbird", "Lockheed's Mark 3 Hot Shot" and "Recce Tech". In addition he has written several articles for the aviation press.

CONTENTS

AIRCRAFT design and manufacture is often a compromise between considerations which seem to be diametrically opposed, and nowhere is this paradox more acute than in the design of a fighter aircraft. But design and technology have nonetheless managed to come a long way during the past half-century, enabling aircraft to penetrate the "sound barrier" and fly at speeds in excess of Mach 1 — something they now do as a matter of routine. Wing planform has changed from straight to swept wings, the use of exotic metals and materials in aircraft manufacture is increasing, and ever more powerful propulsion units are being developed.

At an earlier stage of this evolutionary trail, in the early 1960s, there prevailed a belief that the missile would inevitably replace the gun — if not the manned interceptor itself. The embodiment of this view was first flown on 7 August 1963 by Lockheed's test pilot James Eastman. The YF-12A

Below: The F-4 proved itself to be a true thoroughbred in the skies over Vietnam. But since its first flight in 1958 fighter design had moved on and the F-15 was the key to the future.

weighed in at 125,000lbs (56,700kg) and was armed with just three 818lbs (371kg) AIM-47 missiles. It cruised at Mach 3.2 and, while maintaining 80,000ft (24,384m), employed its Hughes ASG-18 look-down, shoot-down radar and fire-control system to locate and lock-on to incoming targets. The missiles, carried in internal bays, had the ability to dispatch their quarry from a range of 120miles (193km) away. Aerospace Defence Command (ADC) estimated that it would require just 93 production F-12Bs to protect North America.

Almost a year earlier Tactical Air Command (TAC) had purchased the 55,000lb (24,948kg) McDonnell Douglas F-4C Phantom II. Designed and originally intended for all-weather fleet defence of the US Navy, this twin-engined aircraft was armed with AIM-7 Sparrow missiles and flown by a two man crew. At sea, target identification was relatively straightforward and the ability of the F-4's Fire Control System (FCS) to engage opposing forces with missiles from beyond visual range (BVR) would, it was believed, offset any disadvantage incurred by size and lack of manoeuvrability.

The YF-12 programme succumbed to the budgetory axe wielded by

Secretary of Defense Robert McNamara and in its place a major programme was initiated to update and improve the weapons delivery capability of the F-106 Delta Dart. Meanwhile, the F-4 received its baptism of fire in the hot, humid skies of South East Asia.

As the war in Vietnam dragged on, several shortcomings inherent in the F-4's design were revealed. There were difficulties in target identification over hostile territory and this led to restrictions being imposed upon the use of weapons with BVR capability. At a stroke this negated many of the advantages enjoyed by the F-4 and its weapons system. The aircraft's size and its smokey engines made it easy to "eye ball" in a dog fight arena where it lacked a gun, and because such fights were invariably subsonic its speed advantage was eroded. These disadvantages were compounded further by a lack of manoeuvrability when compared to smaller, lighter adversaries such as the MiG-17, MiG-19 and MiG-21.

The F4E redressed many of these deficiencies, but it did not make its first flight until 30 June 1967 and by that time studies were in hand for a new answer to the fighter conundrum.

THE FX STUDY

By December 1965 the United States Air Force (USAF) had received funds for full-scale studies into a Fighter Experimental (FX) design which it was hoped would culminate in a type of similar stature to the P-51 Mustang and F-86 Sabre. Having fielded a Request for Proposals (RFP) for a tactical support aircraft, three contenders — Boeing, Lockheed and North American Rockwell — were awarded Concept Formulation Study (CFS) funding in March 1966, but nothing was pursued further.

Then in July 1967 at Domodedoro, near Moscow, the Soviet Union unveiled to the Western world a new generation of air-superiority and intercept aircraft. Powered by a Tumansky R-29 afterburning turbojet engine, the variable geometry MiG-23 was capable of Mach 2.2 and armed with a twin barrelled GSh-23 0.9in (23mm) cannon, two AA-7 Apex and a pair of AA-8 Aphid AAMs. It had a range of 1,200miles (1,931km) and a ceiling of 61,000ft (18,593m). The real showstopper, however, was the MiG-25 Foxbat whose capabilities were assessed in the West at the time as being nothing short of awesome. This fear was given an element of credence when just three months later a version of this aircraft took the 311miles (500km) and 622miles (1,000km) closed-circuit world speed records held by the YF-12.

The Foxbat was initially conceived as a missiles-only interceptor but as it developed it had taken on the additional roles of air-superiority and reconnaissance fighter. It was powered by two Tumansky R-31 afterburning turbojet engines and was capable of Mach 2.8, a range of 1,610miles (2,591km) and a ceiling of 80,000ft (24,384m). Such impressive capabilities sent alarm bells ringing in the Pentagon and on Capitol Hill, and in August 1967 a second RFP for a CFS was issued; this time the requirement was for a fighter with a secondary, air-to-ground capability.

FIGHTER REQUIREMENTS

The companies involved were McDonnell Douglas (MCAIR) and General Dynamics (GD); both of which were awarded funds for a six-month study. Among the objectives set by the USAF was a speed range of Mach 1.5 to 3.0. MCAIR recommended a fixed-wing, twin-engined, single-crewman platform, while GD offered both a fixed and variable geometry option. Completed in May 1968 this second CFS received FX Concept Development authorization that September, and in that same month the RFP for Contract Definition stage was fielded to the aerospace industry. The bidders for the contract were MCAIR, North American, Fairchild Hiller, GD, Boeing, Grumman, Lockheed and Ling

Tempo Vought. By December only the original companies from 1966 remained, and by now the FX had been designated F-15.

The US Navy applied pressure, contending that a modified version of its VFAX/F-14 should be considered. This issue, however, was neatly sidestepped by the USAF which effectively froze out this argument by defining the overall design parameters in a Development Concept paper. They wanted, among other things: a wing optimized for high load factor and buffet-free performance at 0.9 Mach and 30,000ft (9,144m); a high thrust-to-weight ratio to achieve very high energy manoeuvrability throughout the flight envelope; one man operation of the weapon system for all missions; a realistic air-to-air fighter fatigue life of 4,000 hours; an advanced cockpit layout, displays and controls allowing heads-up operation during close-in combat and a 360deg cockpit visibility; a reduction in Maintenance Man Hours per Flight Hour (MMH/FH) to typical WWII fighter levels; a combat survivable structure, fuel, hydraulic, flight control and electrical sub-systems to enable a safe return to base; a maximum mission gross weight

History and Development

in the order of 40,000lbs (18,144kg); a long-range pulse doppler radar with look-down capability; and a maximum capability of Mach 2.5 at altitude.

Under the Total Procurement Package, a decision to buy would be based not upon the results of a fly-off between competing types, but upon results contained in paper studies, which were also to include details and costs of tooling, development, testing and production.

The project pilot for the MCAIR design entry was Irving Burrows. In an innovative concept, which would later be adopted by other companies, he placed company test pilots alongside the design team at the beginning of the design phase. This ensured substantial pilot involvement throughout the entire design. Bud Murrey worked with the propulsion system team, Jack Krings and Charlie Plummer took on cockpit design and layout, while Pete Garrison became involved with structure and control systems specialists. In addition, these and other company pilots helped market the design.

Having experienced severe cost overruns with the development of the F-111 and C-5 Galaxy, and to allay public and congressional criticism that

Above: 71-0280 pictured after the first alterations to the horizontal stabilizers and wing-tips which improved the aircraft's handling very considerably indeed.

Below: Sporting its high visibility Dayglo orange paint scheme, 71-0280 soon revealed in testing that numerous minor structural modifications were needed.

might be levelled at the FX programme, the USAF devised a system of demonstrable milestones wherein a contractor had to meet specified targets within a specific timescale before further funding was released. All 22 target dates bar one were met on time or early. All bids were submitted by June 1969 and over the following six months the Aeronautical Systems Division (ASD) analysed and evaluated the submissions. On 23 December 1969 selection of the MCAIR bid was announced with an initial contract for 20 aircraft.

Funding for this initial production phase of the programme was approved by the US Defense Systems Acquisition Review Council in the Spring of 1973. The 20 aircraft consisted of 10 F-15As (71-0280 to 71-0289) and a pair of TF-15A two-seat trainers (71-0290 to 71-0291, later re-designated F-15Bs) allocated to Category I tests; plus eight F-15As (72-0113 to 72-0120) to Category II Full Scale Development (FSD) aircraft. It was the predominant programme in the USAF procurement budget. Don Melvern, MCAIR's programme manager, now worked on the project in close consultation with Maj. Gen. Ben Bellis, the F-15 System Program Director.

INITIAL FLIGHT

As tooling up and production of the initial batch of aircraft got underway, so Irving Burrows and Pete Garrison (the back-up pilot) spent an increased amount of time in the simulator. This had been going on throughout the generic design stages; now, with the design finalized, air combat manoeuvring (ACM) sorties, landing patterns, and stability and control work slowly began to give way to practice test missions.

The first F-15 was rolled out officially, amid much razzamatazz, at MCAIR's St Louis plant on 26 June 1972. It was the product of 2,500,000 man-hours of design studies and 37,500 pages of documents. In July it was dismantled, loaded into a USAF C-5 Galaxy and flown to Edwards AFB, California, where it was reassembled and made ready for its maiden flight.

Now that he could actually sit in the hardware, Irving Burrows spent many hours familiarizing himself with the cockpit layout and conducting engine runs and taxi tests. Not only would this be the maiden flight of F-15, it was also the first use of the F-100 engine.

It was still dark when Irving Burrows made his way to Edwards AFB on 27 July 1972. He got suited up in his orange flight suit and collected his helmet and mask — a g-suit was not worn on this first flight. The designed flight profile was quite ambitious and if all went well it would incorporate some high-level work up at 30,000ft (9,144m) and taking the airplane supersonic.

Pete Garrison and Lt. Col. Wendell "Wendy" Shawler had positioned their F4s (call-signs "Eagle Two" and "Eagle Three" respectively) ready to give chase support and just after 0700 hours local time "Eagle One", with the Control Augmented System (CAS) on, lifted off runway 04 without afterburner. Gear and flaps were retracted but Irving Burrows recalls: "A red warning light remained on in the gear handle. Chase reported that the main gear doors were gaping slightly. I successfully extended the gear and decided to pursue the alternate (gear down) flight profile. Handling qualities were performed at about 12,000ft (3,658m)

Below: With its relatively tame shark's mouth markings, 71-0282 first flew in November 1972 and was the platform dedicated to test avionics in flight conditions.

History and Development

where control augmentation was switched off and back on again. I considered the airplane well behaved and comfortable to fly in each case. Engine transients [cycles from idle to mil. to afterburner and back] were performed at various speeds, with no anomalies appearing. Airspeed calibration checks were accomplished against the RF-4C chase aircraft with consistent results [F-15 indicated airspeed read 34kts lower than the RF-4C's of between 175 and 230kts]. Approach to stall and simulated landing was carried out, followed by a normal full stop landing on runway 22 at Edwards. Approach speed for the landing was around 145kts and it was noted that the nose could easily be held off the ground to 75-80kts and then lowered smoothly."

Aircraft 71-0280 landed after a flight lasting 54 minutes. Two problems came to light on that flight which warranted early investigation: namely a high-frequency whine or vibration within, or associated with, the environmental control system (ECS) which was traced to a ground cooling

Above: 71-0291 was one of the first pair of two-seater trainer F-15s which were subsequently re-designated as F-15Bs.

fan and was soon remedied; the second was excessive airframe shake (buffet) when the speed brake was fully extended.

An effective speed brake was essential to the F-15 Eagle since it was required both to accelerate and decelerate rapidly. The effects of excessive airflow buffet experienced by Irving Burrows when he had extended the brake fully had been observed by pilots in the chase aircraft who reported a somewhat disturbing, high-amplitude, low-frequency movement at the top of the vertical stablizers. Such effects were considered unacceptable on production aircraft and so the speed brake was remodelled and enlarged from 20 to 31.5ft² (2.9m²) while its extension limit was reduced from 60 to 45deg. This ensured that the tail fins remained clear of the disturbed airflow when the speed brake was fully extended.

JOINT TEST FORCE

To evaluate and test the F-15, the air force established the first ever Joint Test Force. This consisted of MCAIR — whose primary task as aircraft developer was to demonstrate that the designed performance criteria had been met and to define the aircraft's flight envelope — and Air Force Systems Command (AFSC), which acted as the developing agency, gathering flight data and evaluating the airplane on behalf of the USAF. Flights conducted by AFSC fell into two categories: one studied specific areas highlighted by MCAIR which required a more substantive evaluation; the other consisted of Air Force Initial Test and Evaluation Periods. These were usually two weeks long with each test to be conducted using an aircraft dedicated to a specific discipline; for instance, aircraft 71-0281 would undertake F-100 engine tests, 71-0284 would test armaments, 71-0285 would evaluate flight-control systems, and so on.

These tests were characterized by

intensive flying, following which a report would be written up concerning the particular aspect of the F-15 being investigated. These reports were then circulated to the commander of the USAF Flight Test Centre (AFFTC) and the Systems Programme Officer (SPO) at AFSC HQ. Tactical Air Command (TAC), the enduser, observed all testing and flew a few flights early in the programme for initial evaluation. (Later, they would be responsible for conducting initial operational testing to verify that the airplane was up to the task.) The fourth member of this test force was the air force's Logistics Command, representing the group who had to maintain the aircraft once it had reached operational status.

Below: 71-0291 touching down and deploying the remodelled speed-brake. The lightweight nose-gear leg is particularly well illustrated in this picture.

TEETHING TROUBLES

The AFSC test pilots were headed by Lt. Col. "Wendy" Shawler. On 12 August 1972 he was at the controls of aircraft number one (71-280), taking it on its 16th flight. During it he analysed the aircraft's flying qualties, carrying out throttle transients at 20,000ft (6,096m) between 350 and 400kts and various manoeuvres with the CAS both on and off. During one turn he noted the onset of buffet at 3.1g. Approaches to stall were conducted at 10,000ft (3,048m), again with the CAS both on and off, using 24 units of angle of attack (AOA), at speeds of 125 and 135kts while carrying 4,400lbs (200kg) of fuel; during this he noted very mild wing rock at 130kts and 22.5 units AOA, and that buffet was heavier at 20-22.5 than at 24 units AOA. He considered the one g airframe buffet to be very minor and flying base leg for landing at 18 units AOA to be very comfortable. He also noted that the engine required excessive time to stabilize but that, in general, the aircraft exhibited excellent handling qualities.

In some flight regimes the tail was prone to flutter. This was designed out by extending the mean aerodynamic chord of the stabilator outboard sections, giving rise to its distinctive leading edge dog-tooth.

The aircraft also experienced very heavy buffet during high g turns in the transonic area (.9 Mach and above). Aerodynamicists tried numerous fixes, which included installing different fences at various points on the wing and vortex generators, but all to no avail. Meanwhile, during structural tests it was found that the air loads on the wings were much greater than the design limits — especially at the wing tips. A structural engineer clambered onto the wing and with a pencil and ruler he drew a diagonal line running from the tip of the leading edge, inboard to the trailing edge. A small

gathering then witnessed a mechanic taking a saw to the wing of this brand new multi-million dollar investment and cutting off both wing tips! Carpenters then plugged wood into the openings, screwed it in and rounded it off. When the aircraft next flew it was discovered that the structural loads had been reduced to the satisfactory limits, divergent "Dutch Roll" produced during 1g stalls also disappeared, as did the heavy buffet previously experienced during transonic high g turns.

PERFORMANCE

Maj. Dave Peterson, the AFSC project pilot responsible for performance and engine testing, recalls: "This project was very innovative, as the amount of time spent flying to gather these values was extremely reduced compared to other programmes". This was brought about by the development of two techniques. The first was the use of analytical techniques by new computers which took data from the thrust stand and from running the engine in altitude chambers, combined it with data of the predicted drag from wind tunnel results and then predicted aircraft performance (i.e: thrust-versus-drag) to give performance parameters. When actual test flight data confirmed the computer's figures, then the performance at any point could be accurately predicted by computer, thereby negating the need to fly a test sortie.

The second technique was the use of a longitudinal accelerometer which measured with extreme accuracy the aircraft's instantaneous acceleration fore and aft. Maj. Peterson again: "This acceleration is related to the excess thrust over the drag of the aircraft at that instantaneous flight condition — a point known as 'the Ps', or the excess energy possessed by the aircraft at that point. By making just one

acceleration from just above the stall to the maximum speed of the aircraft, its total performance can be computed at all speeds at that altitude and g loading. By making accelerations at each 5,000ft (1,524m) — i.e. 10, 15, 20, 25,000ft (7,620m) etc. — you can map the 1g performance throughout the envelope, thus giving you the 1g Ps curve, or excess thrust capability of the aircraft at 1g throughout the envelope. By making accelerations at 1g, 3g, 5g, 7g etc at various altitudes you can determine the Ps curves at different g loading. This data is then compared to the computer predictions and used to define the thrust-and-drag curves.

"A typical performance test flight in the F-15 lasted about 30 minutes because we were making a lot of accelerations at maximum power and burning a lot of gas. If I was collecting 7g acceleration data, I would slow the aircraft to just below the speed that

Above: Three F-15A models from Block 11 flying in a classic formation prior to their delivery to the USAF in March 1976.

we predicted the aircraft could accelerate while at 7gs. I would then roll into a bank and increase the g loading while simultaneously selecting maximum afterburner. Now, using the flight path marker and the pitch lines projected on the head up display (HUD), I used the bank angle to maintain an exact altitude ±100ft (30.48m). Meanwhile, I used back stick pressure to maintain 7g ±0.1g. The flight parameters were also displayed on the HUD. While maintaining altitude and g the aircraft would accelerate to its maximum speed for that altitude and g loading. The instantaneous acceleration was measured thoughout the run and recorded in the aircraft."

Above: Pictured four months after its first flight the smooth lines of 71-0280 are still evident.

Basically, there are two factors that affect aircraft performance: weight and thrust. Pushing the technology limits, the F-15 had to meet some very tight weight parameters.

In order to reduce weight the aircraft's skin was chemically etched to reduce thickness to a minimum. After a short while, however, cracks started to appear in many of the aircraft's panels — although none related to aircraft structure, they did cause some consternation among the test force. Design engineers pointed out that by using panels as thin as possible on pre-production aircraft, thickness could be slightly increased where cracks appeared. By the time production aircraft rolled off the line the optimum thickness of each panel would be known, thereby saving weight while maintaining overall strength.

IN A SPIN

The initial high AOA and spin programme was flown by Jack Krings of MCAIR (Lt. Col. Pete Winters was the primary AFSC pilot). Jack had formulated this test programme philosophy over a number of years. It was structured in a logical manner and proceeded in conservative steps. It predicted no spins. However, during a flying qualities test sortie in 71-0280, the MCAIR back-up spin pilot,

Denny Behm, entered an unintentional spin from a full aft stick transonic wind-up turn with the speed brake extended. Both engines stagnated but Denny recovered the aircraft and restarted both engines — thereby re-writing the AOA programme!

During this programme it was demonstrated that the F-15 would not depart during normal manoeuvring. At 300-350kts the stick could be pulled fully aft and using full aileron and opposing rudder the aircraft would pitch up to 70deg and almost immediately slow to 100kts indicated airspeed. It would then descend, wings level and no spin, just a kind of flopping descent. By neutralizing the controls, the nose would drop and again the aircraft would simply fly away.

The only sure way to induce a spin was to use a roll coupling manoeuvre. A rudder roll would be established using full rudder deflection at medium AOA and medium speed. After one complete roll the stick would be moved forward to neutral and fully opposite the direction of the roll. This forced a spin, which initially had to be held in with full aileron opposite the spin direction until a fairly high yaw rate was established. The rotation rate

could then be controlled using aileron. Rudder had no effect; with neutral aileron the spin would stay constant; and with ailerons opposite the spin direction, the rotation speed increased. The aircraft is now rotating about a point well behind the tail and therefore goes around in the yaw direction, with a large centrifugal force pulling the pilot forward against the shoulder straps — a condition known as 'eyeball out g's'. The aircraft achieved up to 132deg per sec yaw rate with four 'eyeball out g's' — obviously very uncomfortable. By applying aileron in the direction of the spin, the rate of rotation begins to slow until, at the slower rates, the nose drops abruptly, the airspeed increases and the aircraft flies out of the spin.

V-MAX FLIGHT

The 160th flight of 71-0281 (aircraft number two) was flown by Pat Henry on 13 August 1973. The objective was high-altitude, V-Max flight. The gross weight was 44,424lbs (20,151kg), the centre of gravity (CG) was 26.1 per cent, a centreline tank and pylon were carried to provide extra fuel for the test and 306lbs (139kg) of ballast was removed from the nose. The tank and pylon were jettisoned over Lake Leach from 35,000ft (10,668m) at 0.87 Mach; he then accelerated to 0.92 Mach and lit the burners. The left burner blew out but was successfully relit, the throttles were then advanced to maximum and the aircraft progressed from an indicated Mach number of 1.4 at 42,000ft (12,802m) to 2.0 at 45,500ft (13,868m), and finally to 2.24/V-Max at 48,000ft (14,630m).

The test programme continued as the design was further developed into the C, D and E models. It is of great credit to all involved in the programme that, despite its complexity and capability, not a single F-15 Eagle has been lost during a test flight.

THE front fuselage section houses most of the avionics, together with the fire control systems, radar, cockpit, nose gear and environmental control system. The central pod provides accommodation for the speedbrake, main undercarriage and four fuel tanks; the forward tank is of the bladder type, the other three are self-sealing. In the left wing shoulder fairing there is an in-flight re-fuelling receptacle. An M61 0.8in (20mm) cannon is mounted in the right wing shoulder fairing and is fed from a 940-round ammunition drum located just aft of the forward fuel tank, thereby minimizing the effect of centre of gravity travel brought about by ammunition depletion. The frames of the central fuselage section, together with the two large variable geometry intakes on either side, are manufactured from machined aluminium.

The wing main torque box is of multi-spar construction. The front wing spar is machined aluminium while the three main spars, bulkheads

Right: By adding forward and trailing edge wing tanks and enlarging the forward fuselage tank, the internal fuel capacity (shown by red areas) of the F-15C was increased by 1,855lb (841kg).

connecting them and the frames of the engine pods are of machined titanium. Two Pratt & Whitney F-100 engines, mounted side by side, are housed in the rear fuselage section. Aft of the forward main spar the fuselage skin is of titanium, as are the cantilever

booms outboard each engine which carry the horizontal and twin vertical stabilators.

Fin and stabilator torque boxes are constructed from titanium ribs and spars. They have composite skins of aluminium honeycomb and bonded boron, while their leading and trailing edges are of aluminium skin with an aluminium honeycomb core.

Wing planform was finally arrived at after no less than 800 variations had been analyzed and some 107 tested in wind tunnels. The result is an amazingly clean wing with a fixed leading edge camber and of low wing loading. A single fuel tank was located in each wing of the early F-15 A and Bs. The lower wing skins are built from machined and integrally-stiffened aluminium.

The F-15 Eagle employs a three-ramp, two-dimensional, external compression, variable-capture area, engine inlet duct system. The front of this inlet rotates about a pivot point near the

Right: This exploded diagram shows the major structural assemblies of the modular-form F-15 airframe, designed for ease of construction. The tail and wing surfaces are interchangeable between aircraft.

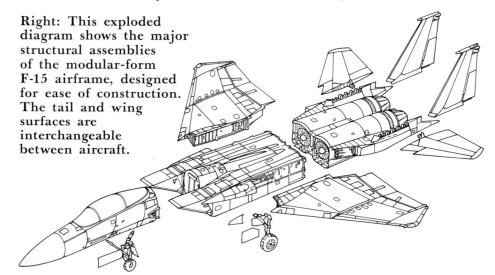

lower cowl lip. Positioning of the ramp and regulation of the capture area are scheduled as a function of Mach number, AoA and temperature, thereby optimizing inlet capture area and achieving optimum inlet performance throughout the entire flight envelope.

ENGINE DEVELOPMENT

At the heart of an aircraft is its engine. The origins of a propulsion unit for the FX fighter can be traced to the JTF 16 demonstrator which was designed in 1965. The USAF funded the development of this advanced technology afterburning turbofan and it led to the production of the JTF 22 demonstrator. The core of this, it was announced in February 1970, was to be used for two turbofan engines: the Pratt & Whitney F100-PW-100 for the F-15, and the General Electric F401-PW400 for the F-14B.

Pratt & Whitney proceeded with

Above: Powered initially by two Pratt & Whitney F100-PW-100 turbofans, the newer F-15Es have two PW-220s or PW-229s.

Below: Ease of access for the ground crews, via a total of 570ft² (53m²) of doors and panels, is the key to the F-15's high levels of combat readiness.

development in March 1970 at its Florida Research and Development Center. (The F401, however, was cancelled on 9 July 1971 when the Department of Defense instructed the US Navy to cut back the planned size of its F-14 fleet; an action which led to a considerable cost escalation in the USAF's F100 programme.) The F100 programme continued at a considerable pace, and by the time the F-15 was ready for its maiden flight it had successfully completed 23 of its 24 critical "project milestones".

Then things started to go wrong: the 150-hour test development milestone, scheduled for 28 February 1973, was missed because of fan and turbine blade failures. The DoD, although not delaying approval of the initial procurement of the first 30 F-15 airframes, made further funding contingent upon the F100 satisfactorily completing the 150-hour test by mid-May. This test was one of the most stringent to which any engine had ever been subjected; the 150 hours of non-stop running involved 30 hours of running at a simulated speed of Mach 2.3 and 38 hours of punishing simulated Mach 1.6 flight.

In order, however, to prevent the disruption of airframe procurement two engine test points at Mach 2.3 were modified by the USAF because

excessive flexing of the first and second stator assemblies caused them to contact the rotor assembly under certain pressure conditions. Inevitably, word of this relaxation of test parameters reached both the DoD and the United States Congress, with the result that the full test programme had to be reinstated and completed by 30 September 1973 (some 14 months after the F-15's first flight). A strengthened F100 was tested in August but it failed after 132 hours while operating in afterburner at Mach 2.3 and a pressure altitude of 40,000ft (12,192m); an engine fire separated the afterburner from the main engine and the entire section aft of the fan was destroyed.

A fourth attempt at qualification on 14 September was stopped after running for only 13 hours 16 minutes when a faulty turbine blade cooling tube broke loose, causing heat damage to some first-stage blades. After other failures, a DoD investigation team was set up and it discovered that a build up of iron oxide had caused serious corrosion; therefore the failures experienced with turbine blades had resulted from the method of fabrication. Further development funding was then approved on a month-by-month basis and a successful 150-hour test was finally completed on 12 October 1973. Deputy Defense Secretary William P. Clements then authorized full funding for both the engine and the aircraft.

ENGINE CONSTRUCTION

The three-stage fan section of the F100-PW-100 engine has variable camber inlet guide vanes (IGVs) upstream of the first rotor stage to provide airflows at an optimum angle for the first-stage fan blades. This ensures the engine's operating stability by enhancing intake/engine matching over a wide range of intake entry conditions. The 10-stage compressor

section has variable stators on the first three stages producing an overall pressure ratio of 25:1 and has a bypass ratio of 0.6. Designed to operate on the ram-induction principle, its short annular combustion chamber produces turbine entry temperatures in excess of 1,316deg C (2,400deg F). A two-stage compressor turbine has air-cooled blades in both stages, unlike the two-stage, uncooled fan-drive turbine. It has a length of 15ft 11in (4.85m), a maximum diameter of 3ft 10.5in (1.18m), an inlet diameter of 2ft 10.8in (0.88m) and weighs 3,055lb (1,386kg). It produces 14,670lbs (65.2kN) of non-augmented thrust and 28,830lbs (128kN) in full afterburner.

ENGINE STAGNATIONS

A problem that dogged the F-15 early in its career were the F100's engine stagnations. When the afterburner is selected, it lights with an explosion. In a turbojet this is not a problem since the pressure pulse that is produced is unable to travel upstream against the

Above: Workers attach test equipment to an F100-PW-100 engine. Its powerful thrust is now exceeded by the PW-229's.

high-temperature, high-pressure exhaust of the engine combustors. In a turbofan, however, the exhaust gas pressure is only marginally above that of the pressure pulse produced by an afterburner ignition. In certain conditions this pulse would travel upstream and disrupt airflow in the core. This would cause a rotating compressor stall and, with fuel and ignition still on, could lead, if unchecked, to a deep stall with complete loss of revs and rising Exhaust Gas Temperature (EGT) which could result in various parts of the engine melting.

To minimize the risk of this happening restrictions were applied: afterburner was not used during take-off; throttles were to be moved one at a time to allow the revs and EGT to stabilize before moving the other; and both afterburners were not to be selected simultaneously.

During a high-altitude radar test sortie one particular pilot, concentrating on his radar display, retarded both throttles to idle at the same time. When the aircraft had decelerated to 200kts he pushed both throttles up to catch his airspeed; sometimes when this was done, particularly at high-altitude, the engines would stall without any external warnings (such as bangs etc.) but he was not monitoring the engine instruments and by the time he realized the engine thrust had not come in he was on the point of stall. When he checked the revs and EGT he realized what had happened; the problem now being that the only way to start the engines was firstly to shut them down. If both engines were shut down, the aircraft would lose all electrical and hydraulic power and be unflyable. The two high by-pass F100 engines needed about 400kts indicated airspeed to spool them up, and in the simulator it had been demonstrated that the quickest way of achieving this with the minimum loss of altitude was to dive at an angle of 45deg then leave one engine in the stalled condition in order to provide the necessary electrical and hydraulic power for the

Above: The integration of the F100 powerplant has created a platform which can operate over a vast flight envelope.

Below: Agility in a dogfight is vital for a fighter's survival. The F-15E's frame is cleared to withstand +9/-3g of pressure.

other engine to be started. This the pilot accomplished successfully and with number one now functioning he used the thrust to level out, build up airspeed, then shut down and eventually re-light number two. In the process of all this activity, however, he lost almost all of his 30,000ft (9,144m) of altitude.

As USAF AFSC project pilot for F-15 performance and engine testing, Maj. Dave Peterson was required to obtain single engine climb performance data. Permission had to be obtained from the commander of the test centre and the personnel responsible for flight safety; thereafter, as Maj. Peterson explains: ''I'd set up just above the stall at 500ft (152m) above ground level (agl) in order to obtain data relating to a single engine climb out at, or shortly after, take-off. I'd then carefully move one throttle to the Mil or Max re-heat position, depending upon the test point. Once stable, I'd shut down the other engine and while holding the nose of the aircraft up, try to hold the airspeed within ±3kts of a predetermined climb speed. Hopefully, this would be completed in 1,000ft (305m) so that I could then take 2,000ft (612m) of data; in other words climb for a 2,000ft (612m) block. Once through that block, I'd push the nose over and allow the engine that was operating to accelerate the aircraft out to 350-400kts. Having shut an engine down at low-level its revs would go totally to zero, so it took a bit of time to break that engine out of the completely stopped position and windmill it up to the necessary 12-15 per cent before it could be started. Only when there-started engine was good and stable could I ease back power on the test engine.''

Maj. Peterson had to make numerous runs at both Mil and Max power settings and speeds between 160 and 200kts in order to find the best speeds and performance for an engine out take-off. During one test sortie that he conducted later in the programme the enormous amount of power available to an F-15 pilot became self-evident: "I was doing some performance testing at maximum gross weight and had gone out to the runway with full internal fuel and three 600gal external tanks, giving me a gross weight of approximately 60,000lbs (27,216kg). This was before the gear was beefed up and the advent of fuel and sensor, tactical (FAST) packs. Because of weight, I was making a Max AB take-off. Just as I raised the gear handle at about 160kts, I heard a loud explosion. Having done hundreds of engine AB test flights earlier which resulted in almost exactly the same explosion — the noise of an AB blow off, followed by a compressor stall — I reacted in exactly the same way and retarded both throttles to Mil to stop a compressor stall. But, as I scanned the engine instruments, I noted that the right engine was rapidly whining down and the EGT was pegged at over 1,000deg C. I therefore had to shut down the right engine. This left me flying on just one engine — which was in the mil range — with an aircraft at 60,000lbs (27,216kg), less than 200kts of indicated airspeed on the clock and the gear still coming up! I dare not risk putting the good engine back into AB in case it also stalled. Despite this, the F-15 was still able to climb at about 1,000ft/min (305m/min) and accelerate slowly. When I reached 5,000ft (1,524m) I pushed the nose over, accelerated to 400kts and tried to restart the right engine. However, as soon as I added fuel it immediately shot to 1,000deg C, so I had to shut it off. I came back still at virtually take-off weight and landed on one engine. When I got out of the cockpit the crew chief asked me what had happened. I told him the right engine had stalled; he said, 'Well it must have been some stall. Look'. When I

looked up the tail pipe all the turbine blades had gone. Seems one blade had come loose and whipped out all the others!''

The stagnation problem was eventually overcome by installing a flame sensor which monitors the pilot flame of the afterburner assembly through a quartz window; if this goes out the fuel flow to the outer section of the burner is stopped. In addition, the engine control system was modified. By monitoring and comparing high-pressure spool speed and fan exhaust temperature, the unit is now able to sense the onset of a stagnation, whereupon an electric signal is sent to the unified fuel control system, which supplies fuel to the engine core and afterburner, and this momentarily reduces fuel flow. Afterburner exhaust is increased in area to reduce the effect of any pressure pulse in the afterburner and the angle of the variable stator blades in the engine changes, thereby avoiding a stall. As a result of these modifications stagnation stall rates dropped from a 1976 high of

11-12/1,000 hours flying, to 1.5/1,000 hours by 1981.

The engines are interchangeable from left to right, or from one aircraft to another without re-trimming. Engine installation is achieved via quick-release mechanical and electrical couplings and access to the engine for installation, removal or inspection is provided via large, hinged, quick-access panels. These features, combined with removable rails which mate with a standard USAF air log trailer, resulted in a trained contractor crew carrying out an engine change in just 18min and 55sec.

SECONDARY POWER

A secondary power system is mounted on the airframe in fire resistant bays just forward, below and between the engines. It derives secondary power

Below: The variable-capture area inlet ducts pivot about a point near the lower cowl lip, thus optimizing inlet performance.

from the engines via power take-off shafts to the left or right airframe mounted accessory drives (AMADs). Engine start can be achieved, without ground support equipment, by a Garrett Air Research jet-fuel starter (JFS) which is started by a hydraulic motor powered from a hydraulic accumulator on the central gear box (CGB). Fuel, electrical and ignition system control is self-contained with electrical power being provided by a permanent magnet generator (PMG) also located on the CGB. For engine start, finger lifts on the throttles engage the JFS/CGB to either AMAD. The system shuts down automatically after the second engine starts.

Hydraulic power is supplied by four interchangeable 55 GPM pumps driven by the AMAD which can be changed in 15mins without interfering with the hydraulic systems. Two primary (PC-1 and PC-2) and one utility 300lbs/in² (psi) hydraulic power control systems provide hydraulic power for flight control and utility functions.

Also driven by the AMAD are two 40/50 KVA 400 cycle alternating current (AC) integrated drive generators (IGSs). Each unit contains its own fuel-cooled oil supply and is protected by overheat-sensing disconnectors. The system also contains two 150amp, 28volt direct current (DC) transformer rectifier units which, together with the generators, provide all the aircraft's electrical needs. In the event of a dual main generator failure, emergency power is provided by a hydraulic motor-driven AC/DC generator.

With the exception of the electrically powered flaps, all of the F-15 Eagle's flight controls, including the speedbrake, are operated hydraulically. The flight control system is a combination system of mechanical and hydro-mechanical control with a dual-channel control augmentation system otherwise known as CAS.

FUEL AND BRAKES

The fuel system is automatic. Fuel can be transferred manually from external tanks until such a time as the internal system reaches the low-level warning point whereupon any external fuel is automatically transferred by engine bleed air pressure. Each engine has its own self-sealing fuel feed tank and boost pump, and an automatic cross feed check value ensures equal fuel pressure and flow to each engine should a boost pump fail or one feed tank empties before the other. All internal fuel can be gravity fed to the main feed tanks in the event of a complete electrical failure. In addition, all tanks are gauged, pressurized, have the provision to dump fuel and are protected with fire suppressant foam.

The tricycle undercarriage is retracted or extended hydraulically. Emergency extension is achieved by hydraulic accumulator release of the

Above: Once plugged onto a KC-135's boom the F-15 receives fuel at 5,500lb per min, making global reach a reality.

uplocks which allows the gear to free fall, then air loads complete the rest of the process as they swing aft.

The brake system consists of a Hytrol pressure-modulated, anti-skid system and hydraulically-operated Goodyear carbon composite pads. Nose wheel steering is controlled from the rudder pedals. The arrester hook is extended or retracted by the pilot via the use of a single pneumatic-hydraulic actuator.

The environmental control system (ECS) provides cockpit pressurization; air-conditioning to meet both cockpit and avionics' environmental control requirements; windscreen anti-fog and anti-ice facilities; together with a liquid-cooling system for radar temperature control etc.

Eagle Technology

A pilot's prerequisite for close-in aerial combat is good all-round vision, and when seated on the MCAIR ACES II zero-zero ejection seat the benefits enjoyed by the "Eagle Drivers" are immediately apparent. Further to improve his out-of-cockpit situation awareness, an ergonomic concept called "Hands On Throttle And Stick" (HOTAS) was pioneered on the F-15. This enables weaponry and radar selections to be made without the pilot having to remove his left hand from the throttles or his right from the control stick. His awareness is enhanced further by a head-up-display (HUD) which shows radar or visual targeting data, together with the aircraft's attitude, altitude, airspeed, heading, "g" loading etc.

The gunsight employed on the F-15 is the Lead Computing Optical Sight System (LCOSS) and it requires the pilot to track the target long enough for the gunsight to use the turn rate of the F-15 to compute the lead needed on the target. An integrated fire/flight control system, IFFC, was evaluated on the F-15 in 1981 and the results were very encouraging, especially with the part it played in shooting down a QF-102 drone at Holloman on a high-aspect pass. The IFFC system allowed the aircraft flight control system to complete the fine gun tracking solution and, with the trigger already depressed, the weapon system activated itself automatically when all the parameters were met. Unfortunately, it was not deployed operationally.)

Detection of beyond visual range (BVR) targets, together with those close-in and look-down conditions that would blind other radars, is accomplished using the Hughes AN/APG-63 radar. After 10 companies had submitted proposals, the USAF announced in November 1968 that

Above: This wide-angle shot gives an idea of the outstanding field of view available to F-15 pilots.

Below: An ACES II ejection seat

A   Environmental sensor pitots
B   Recovery parachute container
C   FLCS data recorder
D   Recovery parachute risers
E   Emergency oxygen bottle
F   Emergency oxygen pressure gauge
G   Inertia reel knob
H   Ejection control safety lever
I   Radio beacon switch
J   Survival kit (under seat pan)
K   Ejection handle
L   Restraint emergency release handle
M   Lap belt and survival kit attachment
N   Emergency oxygen fitting

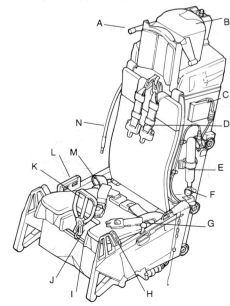

contracts totalling 22 million US Dollars were to be placed with Hughes Aircraft Company and Westinghouse Electric Corporation, beginning with initial funding of nearly four million US Dollars to each contractor under a competitive development programme. After successful final demonstrations were performed by both contractors using a WB-66 aircraft in a USAF-directed flight test programme at MCAIR, St Louis, it was announced that the 82.6 million US Dollars contract would be awarded to Hughes.

The AN/APG-63 boasts three operating modes for close-in combat which provide automatic acquisition-of and lock-on to targets within a range of 10miles (16km). In "super-search" the system initiates radar lock-on of the first target entering the HUD field of view and displays its position; switching to "boresight", the

Below: Due to the policy of low risk development costs, the front panel of an F-15C is low-tech and uncluttered when compared to the cockpit of an F/A-18.

Above: The Hughes AN/APG-63 is easily accessed and since its introduction has set new standards for intercept radars.

antenna is slaved straight ahead and the radar will lock-on to the nearest target within its beam; while in "vertical scan" mode a target is locked-on as it enters an elevation scan pattern set up at right-angles to the F-15's lateral axis. The system has a wide look angle and its X-band planar array antenna is gimbaled in all three axes to hold target lock-on during roll manoeuvres.

A clutter-free, look-down, shoot-down capability at range is achieved by using both high and medium pulse repetition frequency (PRF) wave forms. High PRFs detect long-range targets, but the pulse repetition interval (PRI) is too short to measure range information unambiguously; medium PRFs, on the other hand, enable accurate range measurement and suffer less from ground clutter, but they do not have the power to detect targets at long-range.

The AN/APG-63 alternates these two wave forms, using a gridded travelling-wave tube (GTWT). It also digitally processes data and uses Kalman filtering in the tracking loops, thereby producing the best picture possible for any tactical situation. False alarms are eliminated from the system by using a low sidelobe antenna and a guard receiver, while rejection of

ground clutter is achieved using moving target indicator (MTI) techniques.

The system's air-to-ground modes include target ranging for automated bomb releases in visual attacks; a mapping mode for navigation; and a velocity update for the inertial navigation system (INS).

The APG-63 is fully integrated with the F-15 armament systems. Its antenna search patterns and radar display presentations are selected automatically for the type of weapons to be used (medium-range missile, short-range missile or gun). Complete system synergy is achieved when the pilot, using HOTAS, flicks a three-position weapon switch located on the throttle.

Below: A drawing showing the avionics and weapons systems.

The two fundamental components making up the F-15 Eagle's tactical electronic warfare system (TEWS) is the AN/ALR-56 radar warning receiver and the AN/ALQ-135 noise/deception jamming system. The Loral ALR-56 comprises five antennas (including two forward-facing in each wing tip and two rearward-facing at the tip of each fin), which together provide 360deg high-band coverage. A blade antenna located under the fuselage provides lower hemisphere low-band coverage. A high-band tuner unit provides digital control of the antennas, and this dual-system is capable of scanning a wide section of the electromagentic spectrum. A single-conversion superheterodyne provides high-sensitivity; while dual yttrium iron garnet (YIG) radio frequency pre-selection achieves both sensitivity and the rejection of spurious signals.

The low-band receiver unit is integrated with the system processor, which is a 32k 16-bit word unit with a cycle time of $1.5\mu s$. Antenna/receiver-derived data is then used by the processor for direction-finding,

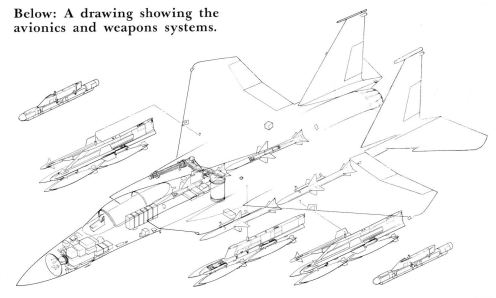

and low-band electronic tuning is carried out simultaneously. Incorporated in the central processor element are pre-processor facilities which convert intercepted signals into digital data and are then compared to known emissions stored in the reprogrammable threat library. In the cockpit threats are shown as a function of bearing and distance from the F-15 on a circular threat-evaluation display; alpha-numeric symbology then characterizes the threat and audio warnings are triggered.

Initial development funding for the Northrop AN/ALQ-135 started in August 1974 and led to a 25 million US Dollars production contract in September 1975 (further contracts have followed). Mounted internally, the noise/deception jamming system utilizes a dual-mode, pulsed/continuous wave, travelling-wave tube transmitter.

The navigation function is fulfilled by a Litton AN/ASN-109, INS and is backed up by ground-based navaids such as tactical air navigation (TACAN), automatic direction finding (ADF) and instrument landing system (ILS). Communication is via ultra high/high/very high frequency (UHF/HF/VHF). The Identification Friend or Foe (IFF) system is equipped with a Hazeltine interrogator.

ARMAMENT

As mentioned earlier, the F-15 is equipped with a General Electric M61A1 0.8in (20mm) Vulcan cannon. Weight savings were achieved by replacing the steel inner helix with a lighter, fibre-reinforced plastic one. This six barrelled Gatling-type weapon has two rates of fire: 4,000 or 6,000 shells/min (spm). Ammunition capacity is 940 rounds and barrel life is 20,000 rounds. It takes less than 0.5sec for the gun to accelerate up to 6,000 spm (and the same to decelerate). It

Above: Four fuselage-mounted AIM-7s and four wing-mounted AIM-9s form the classic F-15 air superiority configuration.

was envisaged that the F-15 would be equipped with a Philco-Ford GAU-7 1in (25mm) cannon firing caseless ammunition, but due to problems associated primarily with the ammunition the weapon never entered into operational service.

The Eagle entered service carrying the Air Intercept Missile, more commonly known as the AIM-9L Sidewinder. This 172lb (78kg) missile represents third-generation development featuring refinements to the guidance and control system which resulted in improved sensitivity and tracking stability. The weapon also incorporated a DSU-1SB active optical laser fuse and WDU-17B annular blast fragmentation warhead of 22.4lb (10.2kg).

To engage targets well beyond visual range the AN/APG-63 radar system integrates with the AIM-7F Sparrow. This semi-active, radar-homing missile is powered by a Hercules Mk58 motor which enables its 88lb (40kg) warhead to reach targets at a distance of

Above: Armourers from the 32nd TFS load 940 rounds of 0.8in (20mm) shells into the drum of the M61A1 Vulcan cannon.

62miles (99.8km) and at a high-altitude speed of approximately Mach 4. The solid state technology used in the AIM-7F, together with that used in the AN/APG-63 (described earlier), ensures that the 503lb (228kg) missile operates effectively in an environment degraded by up to 10 decibels.

STREAK EAGLE

On 28 June 1974 preparations got underway at St Louis to ready F-15 A (72-0119) for an attempt at establishing eight world "time-to-climb" records. The programme, designated "Streak Eagle", also had the secondary test objective of examining the engine's afterburner characteristics at extreme altitudes.

Everything that could be removed was, including obvious items such as armaments, but also the flap actuators, the utility hydraulic system and speed brake among other things. To save about 40lb (12kg), even the paint was stripped off. The empty weight of the

Above: An F-15A from 48th FIS launches an AIM-7. During the Gulf War F-15s were credited with 23 kills using AIM-7s.

production F-15 at this stage of its career was 27,500lb (8,382kg) and Streak Eagle managed to achieve 25,700lb (7,833kg).

The engine was up-trimmed slightly and a V max switch was fitted which provided additional thrust when above Mach 1, increasing total fuel flow by a further 2,000lbs/hr (907kg/hr). Use of this mode is limited to 12min total operating time for each engine, after which the engine requires hot section borescope inspection. Performance figures achieved were therefore due to the low fuel loads carried and not to any major modifications of the technology that was fitted.

Weight considerations decreed that the aircraft should land with just 500lb (227kg) of fuel compared to 1,800lb (816kg) for operational aircraft. All landings were therefore planned as flame-out approaches calling for a high degree of pilot skill because of the lightness of the aircraft, its low wing loading, and its lack of flaps or speed brake.

On 16 January 1975 at Grand Forks AFB, North Dakota, the Streak Eagle's engines were run up to deafen-ing full afterburner, the fuel gauge un-wound rapidly and then, at 2,100lb (953kg), the pilot nodded to a ground crewman. An explosive bolt was fired, severing the steel chain securing the aircraft to the runway, and almost im-mediately the aircraft was at 70kts. Its nose was eased from the runway and the gear handle was raised simultaneously. At 140kts, 400ft (122m) from the release point, the Eagle was airborne and the main gear in tran-sit. A height of 50ft (15m) was main-tained and upon reaching the target climb speed of Mach 0.6 a 5g pull up to 60deg pitch angle was initiated. The g loading was then reduced to 3g and the pitch angle increased to 80deg. Maj. Roger Smith had smashed the 3,000m (9,842ft) world record in a time of 27.51sec in a near vertical supersonic climb!

That same day Maj. Willard "Mac" Macfarlane smashed the 6,000m (19,685ft), 9,000m (29,527ft), and 12,000m (39,370ft) records in one flight with times of 39.33sec, 48.86sec and 59.30sec respectively. The aircraft was supersonic from a standing start in just 23sec! Later that day, Maj. Dave Peterson took the 15,000m (49,212ft) record in 77.04sec. All five previous records were held by another MCAIR aircraft: the F-4B. On 19 January 1975 Roger Smith took Streak Eagle to 20,000m (65,616ft) in 122.94sec and a week later Maj. Peter-son took her to 25,000m (82,020ft) in 161.02sec.

The final record-breaking flight took place on 1 February. Upon reaching Mach 0.65 Roger Smith initiated a 2.65g pull up to a 45deg pitch angle with the aircraft now supersonic. The 2.5g pull was continued for a complete Immelmann turn with the aircraft supersonic throughout. The turn was completed 56sec after release with Roger upside down at Mach 1.1 and 32,000ft (9,754m). He rolled the air-craft upright and continued a slow climb while still accelerating. Just 151sec after release he was at Mach 2.2 and 37,000ft (11,278m). He initiated a 4g pull up to 60deg pitch which he held until his airspeed dropped; AoA was then slowly traded to maintain airspeed, until zero deg of AoA was reached. At about 70,000ft (21,366m) both afterburners blew out. To save fuel he eased the throttle out of the gate. At 75,000ft (22,860m) both engines stalled due to lack of airflow, the revs dropped and the EGT started to rise. He shut off both engines. Cabin pressure was immediately lost and his pressure suit inflated, making precise stick inputs difficult. He pass-ed 98,424ft (30,000m) in 207sec, and holding zero deg AoA he floated over the top at about 102, 400ft (31,212m) and nearly 0kts. The nose started down and the airspeed built. Passing 50,000ft (15,240m) and 400kts the fuel was turned on and the engines started. The throttles were left at idle as he set up for a flame-out pattern into Grand Forks AFB. He landed 10 minutes after release, never having moved the throttle above idle after he'd shut them down on the way up! These final three records were all taken from the MiG-25 Foxbat and they demon-strated clearly the intercept mission capabilities of the aircraft's high-altitude performance.

EVOLUTION and improvement of the F-15 Eagle is ongoing. Internal fuel capacity was increased 1,855lbs (841kg) by enlarging the fuselage tanks and adding leading and trailing edge wing tanks. The company beefed up the undercarriage and, in a highly innovative programme, it designed and built in just 139 days a conformal fuel pallet or fuel and sensor tactical (FAST) pack. Located below the wing and running along the fuselage, it takes just 15mins to fit.

An F-15B (71-291) first flew the 9,750lbs (4,423kg) capacity tanks on 27 July 1974. Flight tested throughout the entire operating envelope they impaired the F-15's maximum speed performance, but impacted little on its overall handling qualities with the exception of one "out-of-control" mode called "auto roll". This was similar to the roll couple spin entry described earlier, except that when a rudder roll was performed and the stick neutralized the F-15 would sometimes continue to roll. Although this was a roll it could easily be mistaken for a spin because the aircraft was going around quite violenty; the difference being that instead of going around fairly flat in the yaw direction, it was rolling around its longitudinal axis. The nose was low and the airspeed high, at about 200kts; a spin on the other hand gave you about 100kts of airspeed with a high yaw rate. If anti-spin controls were applied in an autoroll (such as aileron use in the direction of the roll), the speed of the roll would increase and this could easily lead to structural damage. In this condition control is re-established immediately by applying rudder opposite the roll direction; if the aircraft roll rate is high, however, the aircraft typically pitches over quite

Above: The Advanced Fighter Capability (AFC) demonstrator, equipped with FAST packs, gets airborne. It has undergone many modifications over the years.

Below: The first F-15C, 78-0468, displays the ED tail code while serving with 5612nd Test Sqn at Edwards AFB. Note the FLIR pod visible under the left intake.

violently onto its back and during flight tests over five negative gs were achieved during the recovery phase.

On 26 August 1974, in a clear demonstration of the aircraft's strategic reach ability, Irving Burrows and Lt. Col. "Wendy" Shawler flew the same F-15B (71-291), equipped with FAST packs, on a 4hr 30min un-refuelled trans-Atlantic crossing from Loring AFB in Maine to RAF Bentwaters in Suffolk.

The first F-15C (78-0468) was flown on 27 February 1979. All the aforementioned improvements were standard fit on this and subsequent aircraft, including the two-seat F-15D (78-0561) which flew on 19 June 1979.

To exploit fully the rapid technological advances being made in avionics, the USAF implemented a programme called the Multi-Stage Improvement Plan (MSIP). In phase one of the plan, a 5in² shadow-mask colour cathode ray tube (CRT), supplied by Sperry Flight Systems, fulfilled several functions including built-in test (BIT) displays, graphic display of armament stores, video display of electro-optical sensor systems and weaponry display/ interface in readiness for the possible operational deployment of the Joint Tactical Information Distribution System (JTIDS).

The Hughes Aircraft Company

pioneered the development of a programmable signal processor (PSP) to replace the earlier "hardwired" system, with their 96k unit becoming available to the F-15 fleet from late-1979. The versatility of the digital software system allows new tactics and weapons systems to be deployed just by reprogramming.

As mentioned earlier, the F100 engine required a considerable amount of work to reach anything like its design potential and subsequently it was the subject of a Component Improvement Programme (CIP). The "turkey feathers" that covered the exhaust nozzles of the engine were lost at regular intervals and a CIP test flight was undertaken with all "feathers" removed to determine if the F-15's performance was impeded. The pilot, Maj. Tom Tilden, recalls: "One task was to start at Mach 1.2 and 10,000ft (3,048m), do a level 5g turn and decelerate to 0.8 Mach. I went to Mach 1.2 plus a little, lit the afterburner again and rolled into a level 5g turn. Surprise! The F-15 accelerated! The only way to reach the test point was to go below 0.8 Mach, light the burner go into a 5g turn and accelerate through the speed of sound while in the 5g turn. For an ex-F-4 pilot like me, this was awesome". The

Left: To date, the 21st TFW at Elmendorf AFB, Alaska, is the only front-line wing to have used all versions of the F-15.

Above: The 908th Eagle, serial 84-0001, was the first to benefit from the Multi-Stage Improvement Plan (MSIP).

removal of the "turkey feathers" evidently had little or no effect on the Eagle's performance.

Rows of stub pylons on the lower corner and bottom of the FAST packs (now referred to as conformal fuel tanks or CFTs) were flight rested. During these tests it was demonstrated that in this tangential carriage configuration an F-15 could haul three external fuel tanks, 12 500lb (227kg), bombs, four air-to-air missiles and two infrared sensor pods. This was 40 per cent more than with conventional weapon configurations; indeed, earlier war cries of "not a pound for air-to-ground" were becoming fainter as the diverse abilities of the F-15 were being realized.

The implementation of the second phase enhanced the Eagle's capabilities still further with the installation of a new radar, the Hughes AN/APG-70. The radar data processors memory was increased from 16k to 24k and its processing speed tripled to 1.4 million operations/sec. Gate array technology enables the programmable signal processor to operate 34.5 million operations/sec: five times faster than earlier processors and providing 10 times as

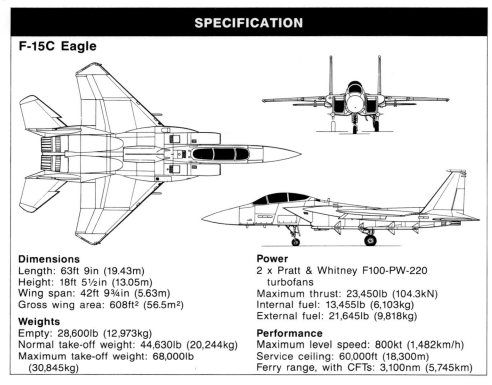

SPECIFICATION

F-15C Eagle

Dimensions
Length: 63ft 9in (19.43m)
Height: 18ft 5½in (13.05m)
Wing span: 42ft 9¾in (5.63m)
Gross wing area: 608ft² (56.5m²)

Weights
Empty: 28,600lb (12,973kg)
Normal take-off weight: 44,630lb (20,244kg)
Maximum take-off weight: 68,000lb
  (30,845kg)

Power
2 x Pratt & Whitney F100-PW-220
  turbofans
Maximum thrust: 23,450lb (104.3kN)
Internal fuel: 13,455lb (6,103kg)
External fuel: 21,645lb (9,818kg)

Performance
Maximum level speed: 800kt (1,482km/h)
Service ceiling: 60,000ft (18,300m)
Ferry range, with CFTs: 3,100nm (5,745km)

much memory. The APG-70's BIT capability has 10 times the software and six times the test targets as the APG-63, and this has led to a 33 per cent increase in its Mean Time Between Failures (MTBF). In addition, the new unit boasts a multiple bandwidth receiver-exciter with 32 coherent channels, including wide bandwidth for high-resolution ground mapping using synthetic array radar (SAR) technology and an analog signal converter. The system is compatible with the AIM-7F/M, AIM-12A (Advanced Medium Range Air-to-Air Missile or

Below: First flown in 1985, the highly ambitious Joint Tactical Information Distribution System is yet to deploy operationally.

AMRAAM), AIM-9L/M and the Vulcan 0.8in (20mm) cannon.

This phase also provided for a JTIDS terminal This system enables USAF and US Army elements to co-ordinate missions with reliable, real-time information by enabling data to be transmitted automatically and securely using the existing Tacan antennas for both Tacan and JTIDS signal reception. The first of the second phase aircraft was an F-15C (84-001) rolled out on 20 June 1985.

THE F100-PW-200

Engine development continued and the USAF sponsored a programme aimed at expanding the capabilities of the F100 engine. This was to be achieved by use of single-crystal turbine airfoils, an advanced multizone augmentor, an increased airflow fan and a digital electronic engine control system. According to Pat Henry, who was now MCAIR's Director of Flight Test Operations: ''Improvements achieved in engine acceleration and afterburner operation were dramatic. Tests included a side-by-side comparison with another F-15 powered by the standard F100-PW-100. The two aircraft started simultaneously, and the F-15 with the digital control rapidly outdistanced the other aircraft''. Another significant feature of the engine was is stall-free operation throughout the flight envelope, even during aggressive throttle transients.

From this programme was born the Pratt & Whitney F100-PW-220 engine, qualification of which was completed in March 1985. It was introduced operationally mid-way through 1986 with an emphasis on reliability and durability. For the first time F-15 pilots could confidently slam both throttles from Mil to Max afterburner and four seconds later enjoy 28,830lbs (128kN) of thrust from each engine without having to worry about possible engine

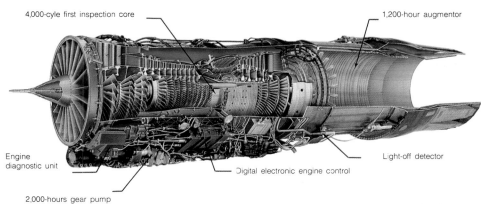

4,000-cycle first inspection core

1,200-hour augmentor

Engine diagnostic unit

Light-off detector

Digital electronic engine control

2,000-hours gear pump

Above: F100-PW-220 Turbofan

Above: Wearing a Europe One or Lizard paint scheme, 71-0291 punches off five 2,000lb (907kg) Mk 84 general-purpose bombs.

stagnations. Such ease of operation is primarily due to the digital electronic engine control system. Other features, however, include a 4,000-cycle first inspection core; 1,200-hour augmentor; and the 2,000-hour gear fuel pump — the latter being constructed from some 60 per cent fewer parts than the earlier model and with a predicted life of three times longer. In addition, Pratt & Whitney offer an F100-PW-220E retrofit kit that incorporates the digital electronic control, core components and gear-type fuel pump which effectively upgrades the earlier F100-PW-100 engine to -220 status at about one-third the cost of a new -220 engine.

Within TAC circles the need to replace the ageing F-4 and augment the heavily committed F-111 force in the interdiction role, and for that matter the equally heavily committed F-15 in the theatre air-defence mission, was all too apparent. To meet this challenge the USAF undertook to analyze a dual-role (air-to-air and air-to-surface) variant of the F-15 and F-16. In all some 400 dual-role fighters would be needed; these would not be additional aircraft, but rather a realignment of requirements placed upon the planned fighter force as a whole. The answer was to lie in the results acquired from the F-15 used for "Strike Eagle". The flight test programme was conducted using two

DUAL-ROLE FIGHTER: F-15E

In a company sponsored programme called "Strike Eagle", MCAIR took an F-15B (71,2917), enhanced its avionics suite, missionized the cockpit and on 8 July 1980 they flew the newly-configured aircraft. It participated in the September 1980 Farnborough Trade Show and was soon undertaking numerous flight trials.

Right: This array of weapons gives some indication of the air-to-ground capabilities of the F-15, developed by 71-0291.

Enhancing the Breed

Left: Strike Eagle with two CFTs, a centreline 1.12in (30mm) gun pod, two AIM-9s and 16 Mk 82 500lb (454kg) bombs.

McDonnell Douglas F-15E Eagle Cutaway Drawing Key

1 Glassfibre radome
2 Hughes APG-70 pulse-doppler radar scanner
3 Scanner tracking mechanism
4 Radome hinge
5 Wide band radar "flood horn"
6 Scanner mounting
7 Radome bulkhead
8 ADF sense aerial
9 Avionics equipment bay, port and starboard
10 APG-70 multi-mode system equipment
11 JHF aerial
12 Pitot head
13 TACAN aerial
14 Cockpit front pressure bulkhead
15 Angle of attack transmitter
16 Electro-luminescent formation lighting strip
17 Rudder pedals
18 Control column
19 Instrument/display panel shroud
20 Windscreen demisting air duct
21 Single piece frameless windscreen panel
22 Pilot's wide field head-up display (HUD)
23 Cockpit canopy cover, upward hingeing
24 Starboard side console panel
25 Pilot's McDonnell Douglas ACES II "zero-zero" ejection seat
26 Cockpit coaming
27 Engine throttle levers
28 Port side console panel
29 Underfloor avionics equipment bay
30 Retractable boarding ladder
31 Nosewheel, forward retracting

32 Shock absorber leg strut
33 Landing/taxiing lamps
34 Retraction/breaker strut
35 Nosewheel leg door
36 Built-in test equipment panel (BITE)
37 Underfloor control runs
38 Boarding steps/handgrips
39 Flight control augmentation system equipment
40 Canopy emergency release
41 Rear cockpit engine throttles
42 Radar hand controller
43 Rear instrument/display console
44 Starboard intake external compression lip
45 Intake negative incidence position
46 Canopy centre arch
47 Boundary layer bleed air spill duct
48 Ejection seat headrest
49 Seat safety handle/arming ever
50 Weapons Systems Officer's ACES II ejection seat
51 Cockpit pressurization valves
52 Rear pressure bulkhead
53 Canopy jack
54 Port engine air intake box construction
55 Variable capture area 'nodding" air intake
56 Intake high incidence position
57 507 Imp gal (610 US gal, 2 309 l) external fuel tank, centreline pylon mounted
58 Intake pivot fixing
59 Conformal fuel tank forward fairing
60 Fuselage/wing panel sponson fairing
61 Intake duct variable area ramp doors

62 Intake incidence control jack
63 Cockpit air conditioning plant
64 Canopy hinge point
65 Air conditioning system cooling air exit louvres
66 Forward fuselage fuel tanks; total internal capacity 1,681 imp gal (2019 US gal, 7, 643 l)
67 Intake ramp hydraulic jack
68 By-pass air spill duct, open
69 By-pass door jack
70 Bleed air louvres
71 Refuelling receptacle door actuator
72 Port conformal fuel tank, capacity 624 Imp gal (750 JS gal, 2, 839 l) each, port and starboard
73 Conformal tank tangential weapons pylons
74 Ventral main undercarriage wheel bay
75 Port anti-collision light
76 Boom-type air refuelling receptacle, open
77 Bleed air supply duct to air conditioning plant
78 Intake ducting
79 Air refuelling feed pipe
80 AN/ALQ-134 ECM system equipment bay
81 Ammunition magazine, 940 rounds
82 Airbrake hinge point
83 Upper UHF aerial
84 Starboard intake bleed air spill door
85 Cannon muzzle aperture
86 Cannon barrels

87 Starboard anti-collision light
88 M61A-1 Vulcan 20mm cannon
89 Hydraulic rotary cannon drive unit
90 Ammunition feed chute
91 Dorsal airbrake, open
92 Airbrake hydraulic jack
93 Centre-fuselage fuel tanks
94 Machined fuselage main bulkheads
95 Wing/fuselage fuel tank interconnections
96 Fuel tank access panel
97 Airbrake honeycomb core construction
98 Starboard wing integral fuel tank
99 Leading-edge integral fuel tank
100 Starboard wing stores pylon
101 Missile launch rails
102 HF flush aerial panels
103 Wing pylon attachment fitting
104 Fuel system piping to wing pylon
105 Fuel vent box

106 Outer wing panel dry bay
107 Cambered leading-edge panel
108 Forward ECM transmitting antenna
109 Starboard navigation light
110 Wing-tip fairing
111 Electro-luminescent formation lighting panel
112 Fuel jettison pipe
113 Starboard aileron
114 Aileron hydraulic actuator
115 Starboard plain flap, down position
116 Flap hydraulic actuator
117 Trailing-edge box integral fuel tank
118 Aileron control run
119 Hydraulically-driven emergency generator
120 Cooling system intake/bleed air spill duct
121 Intake compressor face
122 Airframe mounted engine accessory equipment gearbox
123 Jet fuel starter (JFS)/ auxiliary power unit (APU)
124 Conical intake centre-body
125 Pratt & Whitney F100-PW-220 afterburning turbofan engine (General Electric F110 alternative fit)
126 Engine bleed air ducting
127 Forward engine support link
128 All-titanium rear fuselage/ engine bay construction
129 Forward engine mounting
130 Fire extinguising bottle
131 Engine bay diaphragm firewall
132 Main engine mounting 'spectacle" frame
133 Afterburner ducting
134 Corrugated inner skin doubler
135 Titanium skin panelling
136 Starboard air system equipment bay
137 AN/ALQ-135 system amplifier

143 Anti-collision light
144 Fixed portion of trailing edge
145 Starboard rudder
146 Starboard tailplane
147 Tailboom fairing construction
148 Aft ECM transmitting antenna
149 Variable area afterburner exit nozzle
150 Nozzle actuating linkages
151 Nozzle shroud fairing
152 Fueldraulic afterburner nozzle actuators
153 Jet pipe central tail fairing
154 Fin spar construction
155 Boron fibre skin/honeycomb core construction
156 Radar warning antennae
157 Port rear ECM aerial
158 Tail navigation light
159 Port rudder
160 Rudder honeycomb core construction
161 Rudder hydraulic rotary actuator
162 Tailplane pivot fixing
163 Port all-moving tailplane
164 Tailplane honeycomb core construction
165 Boron fibre skin panelling
166 Tailplane spars
167 Leading-edge dog tooth
168 Port tailplane hydraulic actuator

138 Starboard tailplane hydraulic actuator
139 Tailplane hinge arm
140 Boron fibre fin skin panelling
141 Fin leading edge, titanium
142 Starboard fin tip ECM aerials

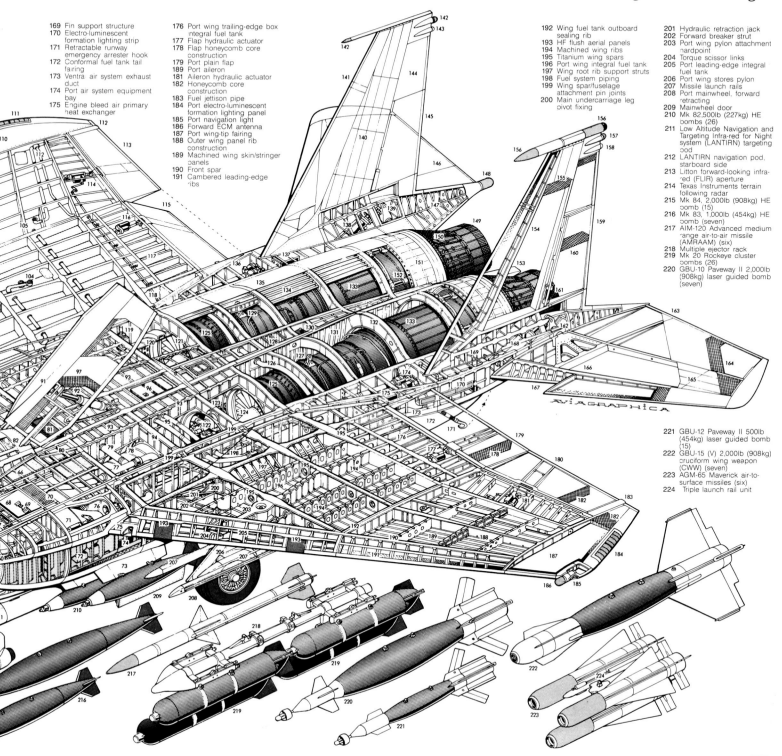

169 Fin support structure
170 Electro-luminescent formation lighting strip
171 Retractable runway emergency arrester hook
172 Conformal fuel tank tail fairing
173 Ventral air system exhaust duct
174 Port air system equipment bay
175 Engine bleed air primary heat exchanger

176 Port wing trailing-edge box integral fuel tank
177 Flap hydraulic actuator
178 Flap honeycomb core construction
179 Port plain flap
189 Port aileron
181 Aileron hydraulic actuator
182 Honeycomb core construction
183 Fuel jettison pipe
184 Port electro-luminescent formation lighting panel
185 Port navigation light
186 Forward ECM antenna
187 Port wing-tip fairing
188 Outer wing panel rib construction
189 Machined wing skin/stringer panels
190 Front spar
191 Cambered leading-edge ribs

192 Wing fuel tank outboard sealing rib
193 HF flush aerial panels
194 Machined wing ribs
195 Titanium wing spars
196 Port wing integral fuel tank
197 Wing root rib support struts
198 Fuel system piping
199 Wing spar/fuselage attachment pin joints
200 Main undercarriage leg pivot fixing

201 Hydraulic retraction jack
202 Forward breaker strut
203 Port wing pylon attachment hardpoint
204 Torque scissor links
205 Port leading-edge integral fuel tank
206 Port wing stores pylon
207 Missile launch rails
208 Port mainwheel, forward retracting
209 Mainwheel door
210 Mk 82,500lb (227kg) HE bombs (26)
211 Low Altitude Navigation and Targeting Infra-red for Night system (LANTIRN) targeting pod
212 LANTIRN navigation pod, starboard side
213 Litton forward-looking infra-red (FLIR) aperture
214 Texas Instruments terrain following radar
215 Mk 84, 2,000lb (908kg) HE bomb (15)
216 Mk 83, 1,000lb (454kg) HE bomb (seven)
217 AIM-120 Advanced medium range air-to-air missile (AMRAAM) (six)
218 Multiple ejector rack
219 Mk 20 Rockeye cluster bombs (26)
220 GBU-10 Paveway II 2,000lb (908kg) laser guided bomb (seven)

221 GBU-12 Paveway II 500lb (454kg) laser guided bomb (15)
222 GBU-15 (V) 2,000lb (908kg) cruciform wing weapon (CWW) (seven)
223 AGM-65 Maverick air-to-surface missiles (six)
224 Triple launch rail unit

Enhancing the Breed

versions of an F-16E, each incorporating a characteristic cranked arrow wing which extended to replace the horizontal tail unit. Extensions both forward and aft were inserted in the fuselage for additional fuel and the undercarriage was beefed up to allow for the carriage of heavier stores, some of which were carried on semi-conformed pylons. Aircraft number one, a single seat F-16 powered by a Pratt & Whitney F100 engine, flew a total of 205 flights, logging 246.6 flight hours; the second F-16, a two-seater powered by a General Eletric F110 engine, flew 182 flights and logged 195.5 flight hours. MCAIR fielded four F-15s: an F-15D (80-0055), a two-seater which flew weapons separation tests in over 22 sorties at Eglin AFB; an F-15B — the flight demonstrator mentioned earlier — which flew 67 sorties over 122.2 hours from Edwards AFB during evaluation of the synthetic aperture radar; an F-15C (78-0468) which flew 91 sorties from Edwards AFB conducting fully instrumented performance and flying qualities evaluations; and another F-15D (81-0063) which had completed 36 operational evaluation flights from Edwards AFB by 5 May 1983. After a close analysis of the results, the USAF announced on 24 February 1984 that MCAIR had won the multi-million dollar contract.

The first F-15E (86-0183) undertook its maiden flight from MCAIR's St Louis plant on 11 December 1986. Today, the aircraft has proved itself in combat and will rank among other such classic aircraft as the P-51 Mustang, F-86 Sabre and F-4 Phantom. Re-stressed and strengthened to clear it for 16,000hrs — double the life of earlier F-15s — this 9g airframe is well capable of hauling a gross weight of 81,000lb (36,742kg) heavenward. A composite wing was not pursued, but the entire rear fuselage pod of the new fighter is manufactured from super-

Above: Ever the workhorse, 71-0291 hauls a considerable load of 19 Mk 20 Rockeye cluster bombs and four AIM-9 missiles.

Below: The 986th Eagle, 86-0183, was the first F-15E. Here she carries four AIM-7s and the two pods of the LANTRIN system.

plastic-formed and diffusion-bonded titanium. This has led to a neater, lighter, more capacious engine bay, brought about by a saving in the number of separate components previously used. Reliable performance was achieved from day one with the two Pratt & Whitney F100-PW-220 engines; while the conformal fuel tanks provided great range at a low drag coefficient which was further enhanced by tangental carriages of stores.

Flight control actuators are driven by a triplex digital (fly-by-wire) system developed by Lear Siegler Astronics which allows hands-off terrain-following at 200ft (61m) even after a single channel failure.

Co-ordinating radar data from its

Below: Tried and tested in combat, this F-15E hauls 12 Mk 84 2,000lb (907kg) bombs on its tangential stub pylons.

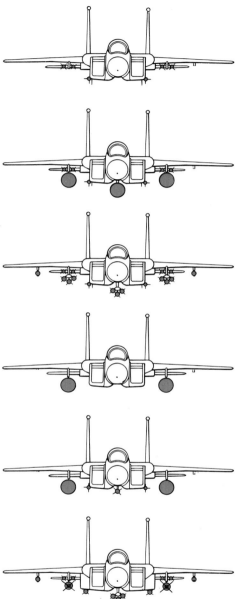

powerful system, an E-3 Sentry crew can direct F-15Es maintaining a combat air patrol (CAP) to strike at targets as they appear; and utilizing their highly-accurate Honeywell ring-laser gyro inertial navigation system to feed position details to the moving-map display, the Eagle crew can set out even during the darkest night.

With the APG-70 the weapons system officer (WSO) has the ability to acquire from a single radar sweep a synthetic array radar picture, even from low-level, of airfields etc in excess of 80miles (129km) range. This picture can then be frozen, thereby reducing give-away radar emissions to a minimum. As the F-15 nears its objective, this picture can be updated further to identify individual targets, such as tanks, missile sites or aircraft on an airfield. The WSO, using his hand controls, can then switch to his Low-Altitude Navigation and Targeting Infra-Red for Night (LANTRIN) system to press home the attack. This system is comprised of two external pods. The first is the navigation pod, located under the right engine intake, which contains a

Above: This F-15A, 76-0086, took part in the multi-million dollar evaluations to develop an anti-satellite (ASAT) system, but it was never to be deployed.

day/night automatic terrain-following radar and a night FLIR (forward-looking, infra-red) which present the pilot with a forward picture of the terrain ahead transmitted on his wide field-of-view HUD. The second is the targeting pod, located under the left engine intake, which consists of a high-resolution FLIR, to provide day/night and bad weather stand-off targeting capability from about 10miles (16km) range; a missile boresight correlator; and a laser designator. The last two are for use in conjunction with Maverick missiles or guided bomb units (GBUs), mainly using laser homing.

To contend with enemy radar guidance systems the WSO has at his disposal an updated ALQ-135 system which now features a broadband jammer called Band 1.5. The antenna for this is located at the trailing-edge root of the left horizontal stabilizer and the

Above: Payload potential, from top to bottom: AIM-7s and -9s; added fuel tanks; iron bombs added to the centreline and inner pylons, and AGM-88 HARM on the outer wing; just tanks for recce missions; AIM- 120s; FAST packs and ordnance on Strike Eagle.

Enhancing the Breed

leading edge roots of both wings. Band 3 transmitters are to be found in the inboard leading edges and the trailing-edge root of the right horizontal stabilizer, thereby dispensing with the blade antenna located below the nose of the A, B, C and D models. Having delivered all its bombs and pulled off the target, the F-15E still retains all the sub-sonic air-to-air fighting agility of its strictly air-superiority forerunners.

The improvement programme is now at the third stage, a massive undertaking which calls for the updating of all earlier USAF Eagles to F-15C standard; meanwhile, over 160 E models will roll off the St. Louis production line. Conversion of earlier models based in the USA is taking place at Warner-Robins Air Logistics Center, Georgia; USAFE aircraft are being converted by CASA at Getafe, Spain; and PACAF F-15s are being sent to Kim Hue AB, South Korea.

THE F-15 STOL

On 3 October 1984, Aeronautical Systems Division's Flight Dynamics Laboratory awarded a 117.8 million US Dollars contract to MCAIR for an advanced development Short Take-Off and Landing (STOL) version of the F-15 referred to as the Maneuver Technology Demonstrator (MTD). Utilizing F-15B (71-290), the objective, according to USAF programme manager, Lt. Col. Richard A. Borowski, was to demonstrate the technology required to operate high performance fighter aircraft from bomb damaged airfields.

Test conditions to achieve the programme's objectives meant that the F-15 had to take-off from a runway studded with bumps up to 4.5in (114mm) high and carrying full internal fuel plus a 6,000lb (2,722kg) payload. It then had to land at night, or in bad weather, without recourse to any external landing aids, in 30kt cross-winds, at a descent rate of 12.5ft/sec (3.81m/sec), and on an area of runway just 1,500ft (457m) by 50ft (15m) when the normal landing distance for an F-15 was a minimum of 4,800ft (1,463m).

Highly-modified, the demonstrator features large, moveable canards on the forward fuselage to improve overall stability. The landing gear has also been modified to absorb the extra punishment received during the heavy lands. The upper wing skins of aluminium were removed and replaced by aluminium-lithium which retains the strength but is 9 per cent lighter.

In addition, MCAIR fitted a system produced by General Electronics called Integrated Flight/Propulsion Control (IFPC) which uses a new computer chip to manage all control parameters. To minimize cockpit workload there are just five modes of operation: "conventional"; "short take-off/approach"; "short landing"; "cruise"; and "combat". Position sensors are linked to the throttle, stick and rudder pedals which feed electrical signals to the IFPC system; control laws programmed into the flight controllers then analyze all pilot inputs to determine what combination of the quadruplex fly-by-wire actuators need to be activated to execute precisely the maneouvre required.

The programme began at St. Louis on 7 September 1988 when the modified aircraft flew for the first time. It flew 42 more sorties equipped with standard circular jet nozzles before two-dimensional, thrust-vectoring,

SPECIFICATION

F-15E Eagle

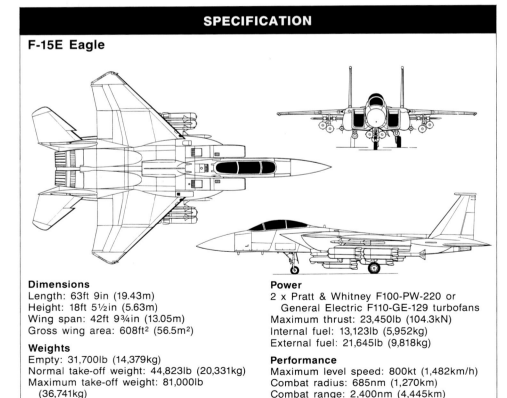

Dimensions
Length: 63ft 9in (19.43m)
Height: 18ft 5½in (5.63m)
Wing span: 42ft 9¾in (13.05m)
Gross wing area: 608ft² (56.5m²)

Weights
Empty: 31,700lb (14,379kg)
Normal take-off weight: 44,823lb (20,331kg)
Maximum take-off weight: 81,000lb (36,741kg)
Maximum weapon load: 24,500lb (11,113kg)

Power
2 x Pratt & Whitney F100-PW-220 or General Electric F110-GE-129 turbofans
Maximum thrust: 23,450lb (104.3kN)
Internal fuel: 13,123lb (5,952kg)
External fuel: 21,645lb (9,818kg)

Performance
Maximum level speed: 800kt (1,482km/h)
Combat radius: 685nm (1,270km)
Combat range: 2,400nm (4,445km)

thrust-reversing rectangular nozzles were installed and ground-tested. Built by Pratt & Whitney these are manufactured from chemically-milled, welded-titanium honeycomb which enables the nozzles to operate at higher temperatures. These lighter units incorporate flat upper and lower flaps which are driven independently to adjust the nozzle profile, and/or vector thrust up/down, and can manage a full ±20deg of movement.

The first F-15 STOL configuration flew on 10 May 1989, then underwent rigorous tests at Edwards AFB during which it successfully demonstrated the thrust vectoring features of the new nozzles and validated some changes made to the IFPC system's software. In December of that year the aircraft demonstrated its autonomous landing guidance capability by landing with no runway lights or ground-based navigation aids. On 23 March 1990 it conducted the first in-flight operation of the thrust-reverse nozzles and on 22 May the F-15 STOL used its thrust-reversing and anti-skid autobraking to land on just 1,650ft (503m) of runway.

On 21 June 1990 ''STOL 12'' took-off from Edwards AFB with Lt. Col. Greg Lewis at the helm and Larry Walker in the back seat. It climbed to 40,000ft (12,192m), accelerated to Mach 1.4 and then flew in a loose line-abreast with the chase F-15A flown by Maj. Erwin ''Bud'' Jenschke. Both aircraft then decelerated rapidly: Greg Lewis used his reverse thrust and achieved Mach 0.8 in just 30sec, whereas ''Bud'' Jenschke took a further 15sec to stabilize to this speed by which time he was over one mile (1.6km) ahead of ''STOL 12''.

The programme ended on 15 August 1991, the intervening year or more having been spent expanding the F-15 STOL's thrust-vectoring and thrust-reversing envelopes, and demonstrating the advantages of the technology in the combat arena.

Above: The first F-15B was transformed as a result of the F-15 STOL/MTD programme which was another Eagle success story.

Below: Evident here are the more obvious external changes — the forward canards and the new rectangular exhaust nozzles.

DURING the Vietnam War the 555th Tactical Fighter Squadron (TFS) ''Triple Nickel'' was equipped with the redoubtable F-4 Phantom, and with this classiest of aircraft they shot down 39 MiGs. With the war over the unit was to be found operating as part of the 58th Tactical Training Wing (TTW) at Luke AFB, Arizona (it is today part of 405th TTW), and on 14 November 1974 its achievements were duly recognized when the unit took delivery of an F-15A (73-0108), the first squadron in the USAF to be so equipped.

The first order of business was to train and qualify instructor pilots in readiness to train others to man operational units. The first of the latter was the 27th TFS of 1st Tactical Fighter Wing (TFW) at Langley AFB, Virginia, which received its first F-15A (74-0083: ''Peninsula Patriot'') on 9 January 1976. By the end of that year its sister squadrons, the 71st and 94th TFSs, had also received their allotted number of aircraft and the wing was declared fully operational during 1977.

EAGLES IN USAFE

The first two Eagles to join USAFE were 75-0049 and 75-0050 which arrived at Bitburg, West Germany, on 5 January 1977. These aircraft, however, were initially to be used to train maintenance personnel. Pilots and other aircraft making up the 525th TFS of 36th TFW were being trained at Langley under a programme called ''Operation Ready

Right: Here flying their F-15As, the 21st TFW have tried all the marks and in late-1991 took delivery of brand new F-15Es.

Eagle''. This marked a significant departure from previous re-equipment programmes and on 27 April 1977 some 20 F-15As and three F-15Bs left Virginia, arriving at Bitburg that afternoon as a coherent, combat-ready unit. The two other component squadrons of the 36th TFW, the 53rd and 22nd TFSs, were similarly trained up and deployed over the months that followed.

Right: The 405th TTW, show by the LA code, has had its four TFTSs reduced to three. The wing commander is nearest the camera.

Below: The 36th TFW based at Bitburg was the first to receive F-15s. It too has now disbanded a squadron, the 525th TFS.

In Service

USAF SERIAL NUMBER CHARTS

Year	Model	Serial	Year	Model	Serial	Year	Model	Serial
1970			**1977**			Block 34	C	82-0023-38
Block 1	A	71-280-81	Block 18	A	77-0061-84	Block 34	D	82-0046-48
Block 2	A	71-282-84	Block 18	B	77-0154-56			
Block 3	A	71-285-86	Block 19	A	77-0085-119	**1983**		
Block 3	B	71-290	Block 19	B	77-0157-62	Block 35	C	83-0010-34
Block 4	A	71-287-89	Block 20	A	77-0120-53	Block 35	D	83-0046-48
Block 4	B	71-291	Block 20	B	77-0163-68	Block 36	C	83-0035-43
						Block 36	D	83-0049-50
1972			**1978**					
Block 5	A	72-113-16	Block 21	C	78-0468-95	**1984**		
Block 6	A	72-117-20	Block 21	D	78-0561-65	Block 37	C	84-0001-15
			Block 22	C	78-0496-522	Block 37	D	84-0042-44
			Block 22	D	78-0566-70	Block 38	C	84-0016-31
1973			Block 23	C	78-0523-50	Block 38	D	84-0045-46
Block 7	A	73-085-89	Block 23	D	78-071-74			
Block 7	B	73-108-10						
Block 8	A	73-090-97				**1985**		
Block 8	B	73-111-12	**1979**			Block 39	C	85-0093-107
Block 9	A	73-098-107	Block 24	C	79-0015-37*	Block 39	D	85-0129-31
Block 9	B	73-113-14	Block 24	D	79-0004-06*	Block 40	C	85-0108-28
			Block 25	C	79-0038-58J	Block 40	D	85-0132-34
			Block 25	D	79-0007-11			
1974			Block 26	C	79-0059-81	**1986**		
Block 10	A	74-081-93	Block 26	D	79-0012-14	Block 41	E	86-0183-84
Block 10	B	74-137-38				Block 41	C	86-0143-62
Block 11	A	74-094-111				Block 41	D	86-0181-82
Block 11	B	74-139-40	**1980**			Block 42	C	86-0163-80
Block 12	A	74-112-36	Block 27	C	80-0002-23	Block 42	E	86-0185-90
Block 12	B	74-141-42	Block 27	D	80-0054-55			
			Block 28	C	80-0024-38			
			Block 28	D	80-0056-57	**1987**		
1975			Block 29	C	80-0039-53	Block 43	E	87-0169-89
Block 13	A	75-0018-48	Block 29	D	80-0058-61	Block 44	E	87-0190-210
Block 13	B	75-0080-84						
Block 14	A	75-0049-79						
Block 14	B	75-0085-89	**1981**			**1988**		
			Block 30	C	81-0020-31	Block 45	E	88-1667-87
			Block 30	D	81-0061-62	Block 45	E	88-1688-708
			Block 31	C	81-0032-40			
1976			Block 31	D	81-0063-65	**1989**		
Block 15	A	76-0008-46	Block 32	C	81-0041-55**	Block 47	E	89-0471-88
Block 15	B	76-0124-29	Block 32	D	81-0066*	Block 48	E	89-0489-506
Block 16	A	76-0047-83						
Block 16	B	76-0130-35						
Block 17	A	76-0084-113	**1982**			**1990**		
Block 17	B	76-0136-40	Block 33	C	82-0008-22	Block 49	E	90-0227-44
Block 18	A	76-0114-20	Block 33	D	82-0044-45	Block 50	E	90-0245-62
Block 18	B	76-0141-42						

*F-15D 81-0066 was later converted to RSAF F-15C 81-0003.
Note: F-15As 72-0014, -116, -117, -118 and -120 were transferred to the IDFAF on completion of the test programme.
**24 F-15s were transferred to the RSAF from USAFE, they include F-15Cs 79-0015, -17, -18, -19, -23, -31, -32, -33, -38, -39, -51, -55, -60 and F-15D 79-0004.

The 49th TFW converted its three squadrons from F-4Ds to F-15s under project "Ready Team". In this programme some of its F-4s remained combat-ready while the pilots of the 7th TFS, and later those of the 8th and 9th TFSs, were trained by the 58th TTW, which had itself expanded to include the 461st and 550th Tactical Fighter Training Squadrons. By July 1978 the conversion process was completed and "Ready Eagle 2", the replacement of the 32nd TFS's F-4Es at Soesterberg in the Netherlands, was underway. While this conversion took place, 18 F-15As from the 1st TFW flew to Soesterberg on 13 September 1978 in Exercise "Coronet Sandpiper". Langley crews were then rotated through this pleasant European base every 45 days, until mid-January 1979 when the 32nd TFS redeployed back to Soesterberg with their new mounts.

Above: Three F-15s from the 49th TFW at Langley AFB over-fly a mist-shrouded castle in Germany during a temporary spell of duty in the European theatre.

Below: The 32nd TFS based at Soesterberg in the Netherlands was the first USAFE unit to upgrade to F-15Cs during Operation "Ready Switch".

During the first six months of 1979 the 58th and 59th TFSs of the 33rd TFW stationed at Elgin AFB were converted to F-15s following the "Ready Team" procedure. A third squadron, the 60th TFS, was activated to provide training support while the 12th, 44th and 67th TFSs, comprising the 18th TFW based at Kadena AB on Okinawa, converted to F-15C and D models.

In Service

"Ready Switch" saw Soesterberg update its F-15As and Bs with Cs and Ds during May and June 1990, an exercise that has been repeated throughout USAFE and Tactical Air Command (TAC). The 58th TTW was re-designated the 405th TTW and received the 426th TFTS.

Right: Bathed in early morning sunlight and awaiting the day's flying schedule, this F-15C belongs to the 67th TFS which forms part of the 18th TFW based at Kadena AFB on Okinawa island, Japan.

Below: This flight-line of F-15s forms part of the 18th TFW which is the only unit to date in the Pacific Air Forces theatre to have been equipped with F-15s.

Above: An F-15C belonging to the 27th TFS, 1st TFW, refuels from a KC-10 Extender while in transit over Saudi Arabia during the recent Gulf War.

WAR AGAINST IRAQ

On 2 August 1990 Iraq invaded the small, wealthy neighbouring sheikhdom of Kuwait. United Nations' Security Council Resolution 660 condemned the invasion and demanded that Iraq withdraw its forces immediately and unconditionally. Five days later President Bush sent 4,000 troops of the 82nd Airborne Division and F-15Cs of the 1st TFW, from Langley AFB, to Dharan, Saudi Arabia. The troops, ships and aircraft of many other nations also supported Operation ''Desert Shield'', but the bulk of strength belonged to the United States.

Subsequently, additional F-15 units were deployed to the region. Air elements of the 36th and the 4th TFWs went initially to Tabuk where

Above: This angle gives an excellent view of the engines and their effect on the aircraft contours. Note the radar antennae atop the left fin.

they formed the 4th TFW (Provisional); and on 27 August the 33rd TFW from Elgin AFB was also committed to Saudi Arabia.

Air activity intensified as units flew hundreds of realistic training sorties preparing for war. On 30 September 1990, during just such a sortie, an F-15E of the 4th TFW crashed in Saudi Arabia, killing the pilot, Maj. Peter Hook, and the WSO, Capt. James Poulet.

In December and January a second front was established at Incirlik AB, Turkey. Assigned to the 7440 Combat Wing (Provisional), it consisted of more F-15s from the 36th TFW in Bitburg and the 32nd TFS in Soesterberg. The executive decision was now taken to enforce the UN resolutions against Iraq and on the evening of 17 January President Bush broadcast to the American nation to announce the air attacks against military targets in Iraq which had begun three hours earlier with Operation ''Desert Storm''.

FIRST KILLS

During the night of 16/17 January, Capt. Steve Tate of the 71st TFS, 1st TFW, was commanding a flight of four F-15Cs which were providing a combat air patrol (CAP) for a force of F-15Es, F-4Gs and F-111s attacking an airfield south-east of Baghdad. Two hours into the sortie, an E-3 Sentry reported a ''bogey'' closing on number three in the formation. Tate established that the aircraft was hostile via its Identification Friend or Foe (IFF) and at 12miles (19km) he obtained a lock-on. Closing in, he launched an AIM-7 from a range of 4miles (6.4km) which destroyed the Iraqi Mirage F-1. At a time of 00:01 Zulu (Z or G.M.T.), this was the first air kill of the war and the first of many for the F-15s. Nine minutes later a MiG-29 was destroyed by an AIM-7

fired from an F-15C of 33rd TFW. The destruction continued when, at 00:14 Zulu, the first double kill of the war was chalked up with two Mirage F-1s downed by another 33rd TFW Eagle using AIM-7s. Later that day, at 13:45 Zulu, two more F-15Cs of the 33rd each dispatched a MiG-29 using AIM-7 missiles.

SCUD BUSTERS

In addition to the blows suffered by the Iraqi Air Force and their command infrastructure, facilities thought to be producing nuclear, chemical and biological weapons were all hit hard early in the campaign. Fixed Scud missile sites were easy meat for cruise missiles, but the mobile scud launchers were a different proposition.

The launchers were detected using a mass of sophisticated technological systems, detailed information concerning location etc. was then sent over jam-proof communications to be correlated and tasked out to night-attack F-15Es of the 335th and 336th TFSs. At the heart of the systems which enabled these F-15Es to claim a reasonable success rate was the APG-70 radar and the LANTIRN system described earlier. The 335th's F-15's were equipped with both the navigation and the targeting pod from the outset of hostilities and therefore were able to use highly-accurate, precision-guided munitions. The 336th, however, only had the targeting pod delivered during the war and were appraising it as the war progressed; they were thus forced to use Mk 82 ''dumb bombs'' as well as Mk 20 Rockeyes. The two units flew an average combined total of 40-60 sorties each night. This was a staggeringly high sortie rate for an aircraft still undergoing operational test and is an outstanding achievement. It was not without cost, however, and the only F-15 losses of the war were sustained.

In Service

DESERT EAGLE

To help solve problems encountered by F-15Es in the field, a programme called "Desert Eagle" was implemented. A team from Wright-Patterson AFB were sent to the 4th TFW (P) to relay messages to the USA about the problems arising, whereupon the technical experts were able to rectify design deficiencies. Sand in the BRU46 bomb rack release mechanisms; sand damage to windscreens; weapon system certification; and additional ground cooling for avionics, were all solved in record-breaking time by this system.

MIG KILLERS

At 10:00 Zulu on 19 January, as the war in the air continued, two MiG-25s and two MiG-29s were destroyed by the 33rd TFS, one Eagle pilot recalling, "The second airplane that came through was a MiG-29. I was never able to take any shots. We had a BFM (Basic Flight Manoeuvre) engagement and he hit the ground shortly after we started". Later that same day, at 19:13 Zulu, two Mirage F-1s were downed by F-15Cs of the 525thTFS, 36th TFW.

On 26 January at 11:05 Zulu the 33rd TFW were again in the thick of it, using Sparrows to knock down three MiG-23s. The next day, two F-15Cs of the 53rd TFS assigned to the 4th TFW (P) had just completed air-refuelling, having been on CAP station for four hours, when at approximately 08:15 Zulu they received information from an E-3 about hostile targets approaching from the south-east. Flying a cut off vector, at between 27,000 and 30,000ft (8,230-9,144m), the F-15s acquired the westbound targets on radar maintaining about 5,000ft (1,524m) at a range of about 80miles (129km). On closing to about 40 miles (65km), the Iraqis turned away from the F-15s. The Eagles accelerated and closed to about 20miles (32km), using their radar sparingly to avoid the risk of alerting their prey. They continued to close and descended. The lead F-15 fired an AIM-7 which exploded near its target, but failed to destroy it. He then fired an AIM-9 which successfully despatched the MiG-23. At this point a second MiG-23, also being tracked by him, began turning to the west, allowing the F-15 to close. Shortly afterwards, lead's wingman fired an AIM-7 at one of his targets which was beyond visual range. Timing the missile flight time to monitor a possible hit, he continued to close. By the time it became apparent that the Sparrow had missed, number two had his target directly under his nose. He rolled his aircraft inverted and as he brought the nose down to sight the target visually, he realized that he had two targets, a MiG-23 and a Mirage F-1, in tight formation. Taking a boresight lock, he fired two AIM-7s and each hit home to destroy both targets. The remaining MiG-23 was now manoeuvering in a tight left turn with the leading F-15 in hot pursuit. His double-kill engagement now successfully over, number two moved wide to leave the lead with a clear shot; an AIM-9 did the rest and another MiG-23 fell from the sky. The two "Tiger" Squadron pilots then went back on CAP after an engagement that had lasted some 8-10mins.

The next day a four-ship formation from the 7440 Combat Wing at Incirlik set up a CAP over north-eastern Iraq, intent on blocking further migration of Iraqi air assets to Iran. Flying his fifth combat sortie of the war, Capt. Don "Muddy" Watrous of 32nd TFS was number four in the formation with the callsign "BITE 04". Just after 12:00 Zulu, while maintaining a loose race-track pattern at 26,000ft (7,925m), they were alerted by an E-3 to a number of "bandits"

Below: Capt. Greg Petrequin took this picture from a KC-135. It shows Capt. Don Watrous minus his wing-tip after having shot down a MiG-23 on 28 January.

attempting a low-level break-out. Setting off in hot pursuit they acquired four targets on radar at a range of 40miles (64km) which were flying at an altitude of just 200ft (61m).

As the F-15s descended, increasing speed to close on their prey, one of the MiGs broke formation. "BITE 01" and "BITE 02" followed him. Another MiG broke formation and was pursued by "BITE 03". That left "Muddy" Watrous with the remaining two aircraft that were by now rapidly nearing the Iranian border. Fire-walling the throttles and punching-off the external tanks his aircraft (79-022) took off like a scorched dog. At 12,000ft (3,658m) and 660kts indicated (740kts true) he fired two AIM-7s: "My first missile hit the right side of the Iraqi MiG-23. It looked like napalm — just a big stream of fire". The MiG crashed just four miles (6.4km) from the Iranian border. He briefly chased the other aircraft, but was forced to call it off as the MiG remained out of range and he was getting extremely close to the border and very short of fuel. After calling the E-3 to arrange an air refuelling contact point in Turkish airspace, he looked over his aircraft and discovered that during the high-speed chase 3ft (0.9m) of his left wing tip had become detached. Despite this the aircraft handled well and he recovered her back to Incirlik without further incident.

On 29 January at 13:25 Zulu yet another MiG-23 was destroyed, this time by a 33rd TFW F-15C touting an AIM-7. On 2 February at 13:20 Zulu a Bitburg bird despatched an Ilyushin Il-76 using a Sparrow; and four days later, at 05:45 Zulu, two MiG-21s and two SU-25s were shot down by AIM-9s fired by two F-15s from the same unit. The 33rd TFW were in the thick of it again the next day when at 08:45 Zulu two of its Eagles destroyed four SU-17s, all with Sparrows. At 09:35 the same day a 36th TFW Eagle

Above: An immaculate four-ship keep each other in visual contact while flying over mist-laden high ground during an exercise.

Below: An impressive finger four formation maintained by aircraft of the 48th FIS during a flight over Flordia's golden coast.

TOTAL MCAIR F-15 BUILDS TO 1990							
USAF		**RSAF**		**JASDF**		**IDF**	
F-15A	365	F-15C	55	F-15J	10	F-15A	19
F-15B	59	F-15D	19	F-15DJ	12	F-15B	2
F-15C	408					F-15C	18
F-15D	62					F-15D	8
F-15E	164						

used an AIM-7 to shoot-down a helicopter. Four days later, another helicopter was destroyed in the same manner by two F-15s from the same wing, again at 09:35.

Probably the most unusual air-to-air victory of modern times occured at 18:09 Zulu on 14 February when an F-15E was on an anti-Scud CAP. It was vectored by an E-3 to a target which turned out to be a helicopter in the hover. Using their LANTIRN system the crew obtained a good laser ''paint'' and took out the target using a GBU-10 bomb.

Two weeks after the most powerful conventional air campaign had been unleashed and just 100 hours after the land battle, the war was over. A ceasefire agreement was signed on 3 March 1991 and Hussein's forces were out of Kuwait. An uneasy peace followed, then on 20 March at 10:50 Zulu an E-3 detected two SU-22s above Takrit which were flying in volation of the ceasefire. Two F-15Cs of the 36th TFW engaged the aircraft and in the ensuing fight one of the Iraqi jets was destroyed — the other made a hurried landing. Virtually the same scene was re-enacted two days later when an F-15C from the same wing shot down an SU-17 with an AIM-9.

With its distinguished service in the Gulf and its record in the hands of foreign air forces it is clear that in the F-15 MCAIR have designed an airplane that will surely rank with the all-time classics. The USAF improvement programmes will modify 300 F-15C/D's and 150 A/B's to include an upgraded computer, the AMRAAM system, Tracor ALE-45 chaff dispenser, Northrop ALQ-135 internal countermeasures system and the Loral ALR-560C RWR. These will ensure that the F-15 remains on the cutting edge of fighter technology until the Advanced Tactical Fighter (ATF) enters service around 2001, nearly 30 years after the first F-15 took to the air!

CURRENT F-15 UNITS

TACTICAL AIR COMMAND

SQUADRON		WING		F-15 TYPES	BASE
48th	FIS			F-15A/B	Langley
57th	FIS			F-15C/D	Keflavik,Iceland
1st	TFTS	325th	TTW	F-15A/B	Tyndall
2nd	TFTS	325th	TTW	F-15A/B	Tyndall
95th	TFTS	325th	TTW	F-15A/B	Tyndall
27th	TFS	1st	TFW	F-15C/D	Langley
71st	TFS	1st	TFW	F-15C/D	Langley
94th	TFS	1st	TFW	F-15C/D	Langley
334th	TFS	4th	TFW	F-15E	Seymour-Johnson
335th	TFS	4th	TFW	F-15E	Seymour-Johnson
336th	TFS	4th	TFW	F-15E	Seymour-Johnson
58th	TFS	33rd	TFW	F-15C/D	Eglin
59th	TFS	33rd	TFW	F-15C/D	Eglin
60th	TFS	33rd	TFW	F-15C/D	Eglin
7th	TFS	49th	TFW	F-15A/B	Holloman
8th	TFS	49th	TFW	F-15A/B	Holloman
9th	TFS	49th	TFS	F-15A/B	Holloman
461st	TFTS	405th	TTW	F-15E	Luke
550th	TFTS	405th	TTW	F-15E	Luke
555th	TFTS	405th	TTW	F-15A/B/D	Luke
4485th	TS	TAWC		F-15A/B/C	Eglin
57th	FWW	TFWC		F-15C/D/E	Nellis

AIR FORCE LOGISTICS COMMAND

		WRALCRG		F-15A	Robins

AIR FORCE SYSTEMS COMMAND

3246th	TW	ADTC		F-15A/B/C/E	Eglin
6512th	TS	AFFTC		F-15A/B/D/E	Edwards

AIR NATIONAL GUARD

101st	FIS	102nd	FIW	F-15A/B	Otis
122nd	TFS	159th	TFG	F-15A/B	New Orleans
123rd	FS	142nd	FIG	F-15A/B	Portland
128th	TFS	116th	TFW	F-15A/B	Dobbins
199th	FIS	154th	CG	F-15A/B	Hickam

PACIFIC AIR FORCES

12th	TFS	18th	TFW	F-15C/D	Kadena, Okinawa
44th	TFS	18th	TFW	F-15C/D	Kadena, Okinawa
67th	TFS	18th	TFW	F-15C/D	Kadena, Okinawa
43rd	TFS	21st	TFW	F-15C/D	Elmendorf
54th	TFS	21st	TFW	F-15C/D	Elmendorf

UNITED STATES AIR FORCES IN EUROPE

32nd	TFS	32nd	TFG	F-15C/D	Soesterberg, Netherlands
22nd	TFS	36th	TFW	F-15C/D	Bitburg, Germany
53rd	TFS	36th	TFW	F-15C/D	Bitburg, Germany

FOREIGN USERS

ONLY three countries outside the USA use the F-15 (Israel, Japan and Saudi Arabia) and two of these have used it in combat on numerous occasions, notably Israel, where it has proved its worth.

ISRAEL

The Israel Defence Force Air Force (IDFAF) purchased their first batch of three F-15s on 10 December 1976 under a programme called "Peace Fox", and their first custom built aircraft flew on 12 October 1977. Since then other orders have followed and they now have 19 F-15As, two F-15Bs, 18 F-15Cs, and eight F-15Ds. At least some of these F-15s are based at Tel Nof AFB and it is believed that the first squadron to be equipped with the type was 133rd Fighter Squadron.

While attending a luncheon at St. Louis with MCAIR officials, a young captain in the IDFAF delegation boasted that he would be the first pilot in the world to shoot down a plane with the F-15. This proved prophetic: some years later, in June 1979, this same pilot was flying an F-15 near Sidon, southern Lebanon, as part of a mixed force of F-15s and Kfirs providing a CAP for other IDFAF aircraft striking against Palestinian targets in the area. An Israeli Hawkeye AEW aircraft detected a number of Syrian MiG-21s rising up to intercept the strike aircraft and directed the CAP against them. In the one-sided battle that ensued five MiGs were downed by the F-15s which returned home safely. Interestingly, this fight was a close-in, hard manoeuvring, classic dogfight using heat-seeking missiles or guns rather than the BVR capacity so often extolled.

Above: Four IDFAF F-15s overfly the historic fortress of Masada. The Israelis have more than 40 and have found them to be excellent combat aircraft.

Right: A picture of innocence — an IDFAF F-15 carrying nothing more dangerous than an external 650 US gal tank affixed to its centreline station.

Foreign Users

Later that same year, on 24 September, Israeli F-15s bounced four Syrian MiG-21s which it was thought were preparing to attack an IDFAF RF-4E Phantom. They shot them all down without loss and again did so within visual range.

On Sunday 7 June 1981 the IDFAF were busy again, this time some of their F-15s provided a CAP for F-16s which successfully bombed a nuclear reactor nearing completion in Baghdad, thereby denying the Iraqis the ability to manufacture nuclear weapons.

A month later an F-15 shot down a MiG-23 or MiG-25 over Lebanon and then, on 6 June 1982, the Israelis invaded southern Lebanon and their F-15s were in the thick of it again, accounting for no fewer than 42 Syrian aircraft when the dust had settled.

The IDFAF's F-15s continue to fly raids and missions over Lebanon and the type looks set to serve well into the next century.

IDF AIR FORCE		
Year	Model	Serial
1976		
Block 16	C	76-1524-25
Block 17	A	76-1505-14
Block 18	A	76-1515-16
1977		
Block 18	A	76-1517-23
1980		
Block 27	C	80-0122-24
Block 27	D	80-0131-32
Block 28	C	80-0125-27
Block 28	D	80-0133-36
Block 29	C	80-0128-30
1983		
Block 35	C	83-0054-55
Block 35	D	83-0063-64
Block 36	C	83-0056-62
1990		
Block 49	C	90-0263-68
Block 50	D	90-0275-79
Block 50	C	90-0269-71
Block 50	D	90-0272-74

JAPAN

The Japan Air Self-Defence Force (JASDF) considered no less than 13 potential candidates before opting for a derivative of the F-15 in 1976. They opted to take 100, of which 88 would be single-seaters and 12 two-seaters, of which only the F-15DJ two-seaters would be built in the USA, the remaining F-15Js (bar the first two) to be built in Japan by Mitsubishi Heavy Industries.

The first two F-15Js (79-0280 and 79-0281) undertook their maiden flights on 4 June 1980 and were handed over to JASDF officials at St. Louis on 15 July. Lt. Col. Hoso and Maj. Tanake flew them extensively at Edwards and Whitman AFBs to evaluate

Below: The Japan Air Self-Defence Force operate six squadrons of Mitsubishi-built single-seat F-15Js and two-seater F-15DJs, about 100 in total.

both the performance and fire control systems before they were delivered in March 1981 to the Air Proving Wing at Gifu AB, Japan, for further test flights.

The Mitsubishi factory at Komaki continues to turn out F-15DJs built under licence and in late-1991 there were six JASDF units equipped with the F-15: 202nd and 301st Squadrons at Nyutabaru; 203rd and 207th Squadrons at Chitose; and 204th and 305th Squadrons at Hyakuri.

JAPAN ASDF		
Year	Model	Serial
1979		
Block 24	J	79-0280-81
Block 24	J	22-8803-06
Block 25	J	22-8807-10
Block 26	DJ	79-0282-85
Block 29	DJ	79-0286-87
1981		
Block 32	DJ	81-0068-69
1982		
Block 33	DJ	81-0070-71
1983		
Block 36	DJ	83-0052-53

SAUDI ARABIA

In January 1981 the Royal Saudi Air Force (RSAF) purchased a small number of F-15s and operated them from Luke AFB as pilot trainers in full USAF insignia. The first Eagles began reaching Saudi Arabia in 1982 and by the end of the year a total of 47 aircraft had been delivered under the "Peace Sun" programme.

The first fighter squadron to receive the Eagle was the 13th at Dharan, followed by the 6th at Khamis Mushayt and the 5th at Taif. Under the peace treaty known as the Camp David Agreement, it was laid down that no more than 60 RSAF F-15s may be based in theatre at any one time;

this figure was observed until Operation "Desert Shield" when the RSAF was increased by a further 24 aircraft (23 F-15Cs and one F-15D) transferred from USAFE.

The Saudis first used their F-15s in anger during the Iran-Iraq War when, on 5 June 1984, two RSAF F-15s from 13th Fighter Squadron were vectored by a USAF E-3 Sentry on patrol over the Persian Gulf to intercept two Iranian fighters violating Saudi airspace. Both the F-15s launched AIM-7s and were able to claim a kill each — the intruders, ironically, were F-4E Phantoms.

Nearly seven years later, on 24 January 1991, Saudi Arabia was a participant in the coalition against Iraq and a USAF E-3 had detected two Iraqi Mirage F-1s flying at high-speed and low-level southwards along the Persian Gulf coast. Capt. Ayhed Salah Al-Shamrani was leading a flight of four RSAF F-15s on a CAP when he was vectored to intercept the intruders that were 80 miles away (129km) and heading in the opposite direction. Ordering two of the four F-15s to remain on CAP, he and his wingman set off in pursuit. No attempt was made by the Iraqis to evade the F-15s, until

Above: This F-15D was the first to be delivered to the Saudi Arabians. It is operated by 13th Sqn from Dharan. It is ironic that the Saudi F-15's first kills in combat were F-4 Phantoms.

the last minute when one F-1 jettisoned its ordnance — believed to have been an Exocet anti-ship missile. They then commenced a left bank but the AIM-9s fired by Shamrani slammed into their targets and destroyed both aircraft.

ROYAL SAUDI AIR FORCE		
Year	Model	Serial
1980		
Block 27	D	80-0107-10
Block 28	C	80-0062-67
Block 28	D	80-0111-12
Block 29	C	80-0068-74
Block 29	D	80-0113-14
1981		
Block 30	C	80-0075-85
Block 30	D	80-0115-17
Block 31	C	80-0086-99
Block 31	D	80-0118-99
Block 32	C	80-0100-06
Block 32	C	81-0002-03
Block 32	D	80-0120-21

INDEX